developing
Numeracy
Skills

NUMERACY

KEY STAGE 1: YEAR 2/ PRIMARY 3

SUE ATKINSON

Contents

Published by Hopscotch Educational Publishing Ltd,
Althorpe House, Althorpe Street, Leamington Spa CV31 2AU.

© 1999 Hopscotch Educational Publishing

Written by Sue Atkinson
Series design by Blade Communications
Illustrated by Jean de Lamos
Cover illustration by Claire Boyce
Printed by Clintplan, Southam

Sue Atkinson hereby asserts her moral right to be identified as
the author of this work in accordance with the Copyright,
Designs and Patents Act, 1988.

ISBN 1-902239-32-6

ABOUT THE SERIES

Developing Numeracy Skills is a series of books aimed at developing the basic skills of the 'Framework for teaching mathematics'. There is one book for each year from Reception (Scottish Primary 1), through Key Stage 1 to the end of Key Stage 2 (Scottish Primary 7).

The series offers a structured approach which provides detailed lesson plans to teach specific numeracy skills. A unique feature of the series is the provision of differentiated photocopiable activities which are aimed at considerably reducing teacher preparation time.

ABOUT THIS BOOK

This book is for teachers of Year 2 children and Scottish level P3. It aims to:

- give emphasis to those aspects of numeracy that teachers on the National Numeracy Project found to be crucial to raising the standards of numeracy in their classrooms
- support a three-fold structured lesson for maximising learning to raise standards
- support teachers in developing children's flexible methods of calculating
- encourage a wide range of mathematical vocabulary by giving some key questions to ask
- support teachers with a wide range of mental maths questions to develop good mental recall with children

Throughout the book the maths is set in the context of pirates, but you can adapt the lessons by using your own topic.

(You will find that the content for the Reception/ P1 and the Y1/P2 book in this series is structured in a similar way to assist you if you have a mixed-age class.)

CHAPTER CONTENT

 ### Overall learning objectives

Each chapter has two lesson plans and the overall learning objectives outline the aims for both lessons and the further activities in each chapter.

 ### Assessment focus

This sets out the specific learning objective that you will be able to assess for each individual lesson within the chapter. (See page 4 for more on assessment.)

 ### Resources

This is a list of what you will need to do the lessons.

 ### Oral work and mental calculation

This section is a 'mental maths warm up' and can sometimes have a different learning objective from the main lesson plan. It gives you ideas for how to develop quick mental recall with your children, so keeping key ideas ticking over and giving them the extra practice they need to be confident. You can 'mix and match' these to suit your lesson. So, you might want to do number bonds to 10 every day for a fortnight, even when your main lesson is about measuring, or you might want to recap something about shape and space on a day when the main lesson is about number, and so on. This part of the lesson is usually about 5 to 10 minutes long.

Starting point: whole class

This provides ideas for introducing the activity and may include key questions to ask the children so that they can move on to their group task having been introduced to concepts and the vocabulary they will need for the group activities. This starting point is usually about 10 minutes long, depending on the task.

Group activities

This explains the tasks that the children will do. The 'Focus Group' works with you and this group alternates between the different ability groups. The section on 'teacher independent groups' gives three tasks that can be done more or less independently of you. Sometimes you might only use two of the three independent tasks because one group is the focus group. The Group 1 tasks are the easiest and the Group 3 tasks the hardest. For Year 2/P3 children, this section is about 10 or 20 minutes long, depending on the task. Many of these teacher independent tasks are

Numeracy
Year 2/P3

developing
Numeracy
Skills

3

©Hopscotch Educational Publishing

maths games. Games give plenty of practice with the learning objective, help the children to learn the language associated with the concept you are teaching, and can provide the incentive to keep working while you are busy with your focus group.

Using the differentiated activity sheets

Activity 1 is for the children who are likely to struggle with the content of the lesson and who need a simple task, often with lower numbers than other groups. Activity 2 is for children who seem to have grasped the main ideas during the whole class starter. Activity 3 is for those who need a more challenging task.

The book symbol at the bottom of some activity pages is for further work to be done in maths books, but unless you have a helper, sometimes this might be the time to suggest a maths game is played. (See the generic sheets at the back of the book.)

Plenary session

This suggests ideas for a whole-class review to discuss the learning outcomes and gives questions to ask so that children have a chance to reflect on what they have learned and for the teacher to assess. This section is often about 5 or 10 minutes.

Further activities

This is a list of further activities that can be developed from the lessons to give children more experience with the learning objectives. Some of these could be used for homework.

Extension

These are ideas for how to take children on and give them more difficult tasks.

Support

These are ideas for children who are going to need more support before they have grasped the learning objectives.

The use of calculators

Although children will not be using calculators very much in Key Stage 1, and they will certainly not use them for calculating, they can be very helpful indeed in focusing children on to number patterns, place value and so on. In Year 2, calculators are invaluable for teaching number recognition and an understanding of conventional symbols such as the addition sign. We need them there in the classroom, in the play shop, and so on, so that children are free to explore the wonder and excitement of number that can only come through using these powerful tools.

 GENERIC SHEETS

At the back of the book there are some generic sheets that give extra help with key skills for Year 2 children. These sheets can be photocopied with different numbers on them to suit your different groups. Guidance on using them is given in the lesson plans or in the further activities.

 ASSESSMENT

You will notice at the top of each activity sheet there is a row of three small boxes. These link with your assessment of how well the child has grasped the intended learning for that lesson. On page 5 there is a list of the assessment criteria for both lessons for each chapter (the ones for the activity sheets are in italics). You can use these criteria to decide how well a child has grasped the content of a particular lesson.

+ If they seem not to have grasped the concept, tick the first box.
+ If there is evidence of the child having learned what you intended tick the second box.
+ Tick the third box for children who have a very secure grasp of the lesson and you think can use and apply the concept.

Of course, often the evidence (or lack of it) on the sheet will not correspond with your observations of some children's understandings during oral maths times and when you work with your focus group. (And sometimes your learning objective will be about ability to use mathematical language, such as in Chapter 3, Lesson One.) So you will need to make a note (on the sheet if you want) of what

Introduction

those children said or did to back up why you ticked a particular box. With young children, recording on sheets is often not going to assess their understanding, especially where the lesson is about some acquisition of essential mathematical language. We need to listen to children very carefully as they respond to the activity and we need to use prompting and probing questions in order to be clear about what each individual understands. Assessment is much broader than children's recordings, so your additional annotations based on your observations are important.

At the end of each half term, flicking through each child's sheets can give you a basis for your teacher assessments, and will enable you to plan for your next half term.

In addition to this assessment on the children's sheets, there is a self-assessment sheet on page 96. The blank spaces are for you and the child to record specific targets that the child has achieved. The children will need to reflect on their learning; for example they need to think of a favourite way to add two-digit numbers and think about what they would like to be better at in maths.

Year 2 Assessment Criteria

Chapter 1
+ Can develop and recognise a pattern.
+ *Can estimate positions on number line.*

Chapter 2
+ Can partition into tens and units.
+ *Can understand grouping in 10s.*

Chapter 3
+ Can talk about a general statement.
+ *Can describe and extend number sequences.*

Chapter 4
+ Can partition to aid addition calculations.
+ *Can check addition in various ways.*

Chapter 5
+ Can partition numbers to aid subtraction.
+ *Can use vocabulary/say/write subtraction and corresponding addition facts.*

Chapter 6
+ Can add/subtract 9/11 by adding/subtracting 10 then adjusting.
+ *Can partition into 5 and a bit when adding then recombine.*

Chapter 7
+ *Can use knowledge that numbers can be added in any order to add 3 numbers.*
+ Can choose from a range of ways of calculating and explain methods.

Chapter 8
+ *Can understand equal grouping and use 'lots of'.*
+ Can understand equal grouping and use language of sharing.

Chapter 9
+ *Can exchange pennies for higher values.*
+ Can use appropriate operations.

Chapter 10
+ Can explain how a problem was solved.
+ *Can recognise equivalent fractions.*

Chapter 11
+ Can use a ruler/metre stick appropriately.
+ *Can read a scale.*

Chapter 12
+ *Can sort numbers into appropriate sets.*
+ Can solve a problem by using data.

Chapter 13
+ Can recognise a line of symmetry.
+ *Can relate 3D shapes to pictures of them.*

Chapter 14
+ Can identify right angles.
+ *Can give instructions for a route.*

The criteria in italics are those that relate to the children's activity sheets.

Counting and estimating

◆ Overall learning objectives

◆ Develop and recognise a pattern.
◆ Use approximation to do calculations.
◆ Estimate positions of numbers on a number line.
◆ Round a number to the nearest 10 or 100.

◆ LESSON ONE NUMBER PATTERNS

◆ Assessment focus

Can the children develop and recognise a pattern?

◆ Resources

◆ 100 square or large piece of blank paper
◆ Post-it notes or Blu-tack
◆ number lines to 100

◆ Oral work and mental calculation

Adding and subtracting tens

◆ Give practice with adding 10 to any number under 100. Add 10 repeatedly, focusing on this pattern: 2, 12, 22, 32, 42 and so on, counting back again as well. Demonstrate these jumps of 10 on a number line.

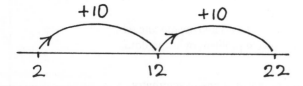

◆ Starting point: whole class

◆ Make a large 10 x 10 grid on paper making each square about the size of a square Post-it note. If you already have a large 100 square, start by covering each number with Blu-tacked paper. (The grid can be either 1–100 or as 0–99. Using Post-its or Blu-tacked numbers means you can

repeat the activity.) Ask the children to choose a number and tell you where to write it on the 100 square. Then ask some children to come up and write more numbers. Ask them how they know where a number is. Look for explanations about rows with the numbers that start with 3 tens, or where children explain about the vertical pattern of the same number in the units.

◆ Now develop some patterns.

   4 count on 5 is 9 so
   14 count on 5 is 19 and
   24 count on 5 is 29.

Say "We don't need to count on now. We can see a pattern. Who can use the pattern to predict what 34 add 5 is?" Make sure your special needs children are understanding, so that they know the answer must end in a 9.

◆ Repeat this with something similar, for example 5 count on 3. 'What will the answer end with? How many units? So what about 15 count on 3 and 25 count on 3?" Invite one child to explain the vertical pattern that is developing.

◆ Group activities

 Focus group

Give some pattern starters, e.g. 1+ 5 = 6, 11+ 5 = 16 and ask children to tell you about the pattern. When they seem reasonably confident, they make up a pattern of their own. Assess understanding of what a pattern is and ability to develop it. Encourage some children to go on beyond 100. They can write out the start of a pattern to take to review time for others to finish.

 Teacher independent groups

Group 1: Provide a 100 square (generic sheet 1 on page 90) and the start of a pattern that goes down the 100 square vertically, such as :

   1 + 3 = 4
   11 + 3 = 14
   21 + 3 =   and so on.

The children should finish the pattern on the 100 square by circling the numbers.

Counting and estimating

Group 2: Give this group about four patterns to continue up to or beyond a 100, for example:

$$7 + 8 = 15$$
$$17 + 8 = 25$$

Group 3: If this group can manage it, give them a pattern starter that will go above 100, for example:

$$75 + 5 =$$
$$175 + 5 =$$

Ask them to make up at least one of their own patterns for everyone to solve at review time.

 Plenary session

✦ The focus group can introduce their patterns and ask others to continue them.
✦ Ask groups 1 and 2 to describe their patterns and to tell you what a pattern is.
✦ Keep emphasising that they can use things they already know to find out new things, for example 3 + 6 is 9, so 30 + 60 is 90. This leads into group 3 showing their patterns for others to solve.

LESSON TWO ✦ ESTIMATING & ROUNDING

 Assessment focus

Can the children estimate positions of numbers on a number line?

 Resources

✦ numbered yoghurt pots

 Oral work and mental calculation

Estimating positions on a number line

✦ Ask the children to imagine that you are zero and the wall is 10 on a number line. Using the numbered yoghurt pots, say *"So where would we put the yoghurt pot with 5 on it? Where would 3 be, and 7?"* Invite them to place the pots. Now change the line so that the wall is 20. *"Where would 5 be now? What about 10? If we have the wall as 100, where would 50 be? What about 20/30/90?"* Establish the multiples of 10 then try positioning children on the line, establishing that 37 would be very close to 40 and so on. *"If I'm 20 and the wall is 30 what number is half way between? Could we fit 15 on that line?"* (No, but any number line

can be extended in both directions.) If you wish, you could use coloured sticky tape on the floor to make a semi-permanent line.

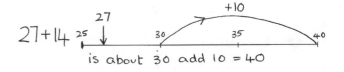 **Starting point: whole class**

✦ Continue with the oral activity. Using a line from 0 to 50, put on all the multiples of 10 and also the half way mark, 25. Then move on to numbers such as 31; it would be very close to 30. Explain that when we calculate, it is often very useful to round numbers to the nearest multiple of 10, so 21 add 31 is adding about 20 to about 30, so our answer ought to be about 50. (You could do all the calculating using approximations in another lesson.) Do some work with adding using numbers such as 29 and 37, rounding to the nearest multiple of 10.
✦ Take numbers that end in 5 up to the next 10 so that 35 is rounded up to 40.
✦ Demonstrate marking on a number line on the board as the children will do on the activity sheets.

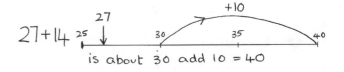

Counting and estimating

✦ Group activities

Focus group

Continue with the starter activity, using a wide range of language. Go over rounding up numbers with 5 in the units. (Now or later do some more approximating for calculating, for example 28 add 38 would be an answer somewhere just a bit under 30 plus 40.) Ask the children to record positions on empty number lines like the other groups. (Use generic sheet 3 on page 92.)

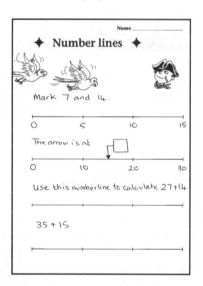

Teacher independent groups

Use the photocopiable activity sheets

Activity sheet 1: If children need the support let them start with a set of number cards 0 to 10 and order them before they start. Have a number line to 100 on display nearby.

Activity sheet 2: Challenge these children to do the activity without reference to the wall number line. Not all these number lines start at 0.

Activity sheet 3: Only the first line starts with zero.

✦ Plenary session

✦ Let the children compare their work in pairs and come and demonstrate some of their lines on the board. Ask questions such as *"How did you know that was where to put 85?" "Do you think Dan is right to put 25 there?" "Now you've had more time to think about it, does anyone want to move any of their numbers?"*

✦ Try to bring out the approximating that the children will have needed to use. For example, *"If that is 100, then 50 must be round about there, so 65 would be a little further along towards 100."*

✦ Further activities

✦ Make some marks on number lines like this and ask for estimates of what the numbers could be. On this line, the arrow would be 15.

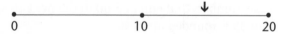

✦ Continue to use rounding to find approximate answers to calculations, for example 29 add 17 is almost 30 add almost 20, so the answer must be a bit less than 50. Then work out how many less and count back.

✦ Extension

✦ Use generic sheet 2 (page 91) to give practice with understanding the layout of number

squares by cutting up the 100 square and leaving some spaces blank. The children then fill in the numbers and position the sections together to make a number square. Don't always use 10 by 10 spaces.

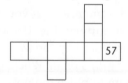

"Fill in the missing numbers on this bit of a 100 square."

✦ Support

✦ Give restricted sets of number cards to 20, 50 or 100, such as some multiples of 10, and ask the children to order them and position them.

◆ Find the numbers ◆

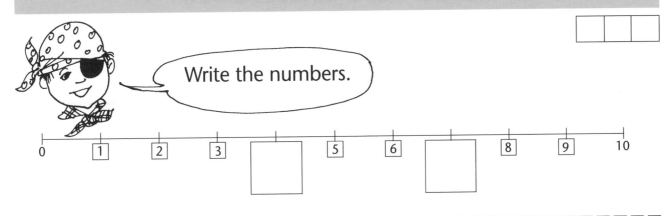

Write the numbers.

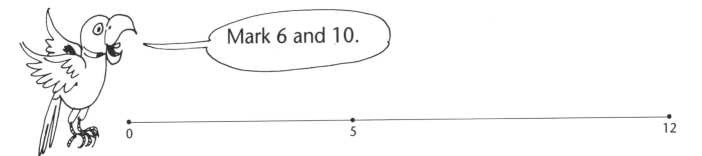

Mark 6 and 10.

Mark 4 and 9.

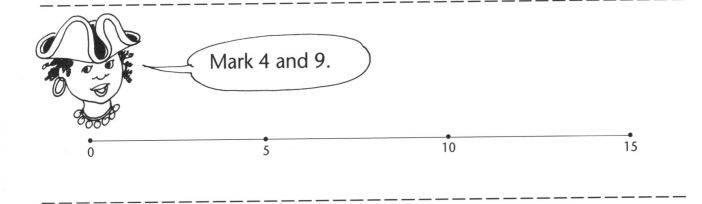

◆ Put some numbers on this line.

 Draw a line 0 to 100 and mark these numbers on it.

10, 20, 30, 40, 50, 60, 70, 80, 90.

✦ Find the numbers ✦

Mark 5, 10 and 15.

0   20

Mark 40, 50, 60 and 70.

0   100

Mark 20, 30, 40, 50, 60, 70, 80 and 90.

0   100

Mark 25, 35, 45 and 55.

20   60

Put some numbers on this line.

Draw a line 0 to 200 and mark on it 50, 100 and 150.

developing
Numeracy Skills

Photocopiable

✦ Find the numbers ✦

Mark 40, 50 and 70.

0 ————————————————————————— 100

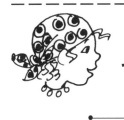

Mark 75, 85 and 95.

60 ————————————————————————— 100

Mark 65, 70, 75 and 85.

50 ————————————————————————— 90

Put some numbers on this line.

————————————————————————————

✦ Draw a line and mark some numbers.

 Draw a line 0 to 1000 and mark on it 500, 550, 750, 800 and 950.

Place value and ordering

 ### Overall learning objectives

✦ Partition 2 digit numbers into tens and ones.
✦ Recognise doubles.
✦ Put numbers on an abacus.
✦ Count up to 100 by grouping.
✦ Order numbers.
✦ Understand that money is grouped in 10s.
✦ Begin to use pound and penny notation with a decimal point.

LESSON ONE
HOW MANY?

 ### Assessment focus

Can the children partition a 2 digit number into tens and units?

 ### Resources

✦ bean bags
✦ abacuses
✦ lots of pennies, 10 pence coins, pound coins
✦ 1–6 dice
✦ place value boards
✦ tens and units spinners or dice
✦ 100 squares
✦ tens and units rods (Dienes or Cuisenaire)

 ### Oral work and mental calculation

Ordering numbers

✦ Write numbers on cards or paper and hang them on a washing line out of order. (This can be done with both a complete series of numbers, for example 13 to 27, or an incomplete set.) Put the numbers in order and ask *"What is the fourth number in our line of numbers?"*

 ✦ *"Tell me a number that is between 21 and 31." "Is 37 more than or less than 73?" "Tell me a number that is more than 24."*

 ### Starting point: whole class

✦ Sit the children in a circle around a fairly large paper target, which has tens in one part and ones in another part. Choose some children to throw 3 bean bags on to the target adding up their score.

Fran scored 21.

✦ Identify the numbers in tens and units and write them on the board. Demonstrate the numbers on an abacus, with ten pence coins and pennies and with ten rods and unit rods.
✦ *"56 pennies have the same value as 5 ten pence pieces and 6 one pence pieces. We can make 56 on an abacus like this."*

 ### Group activities

 **Focus group**

With your help, these children should play the starter game again and record their score and make each one on an abacus. You could race to a 100 or see who has the largest score after 3 throws each.

 Teacher independent groups

Group 1: Provide each pair of children in this group with about 3 number cards of 2 digit numbers, such as 34, 51 and 26. They must circle their numbers on a 100 square (generic sheet 1 on page 90) and make the numbers with tens and units rods.

Place value and ordering

Group 2: Provide a 100 square and tens and units spinners or dice. In pairs, the children take turns to spin or throw the dice. They then tell their partner the name of their number. *"My tens spinner is 3 and my units spinner is 7 so that makes 37."* They circle the number on the 100 square and then make the number in some other way, such as on an abacus. (There is space on the 100 square sheet to draw some abacuses for children to record their numbers.)

tens	ones

Group 3: These children do the same as group 2 but use a blank 100 square (generic sheet 2 on page 91). They have to position their numbers on their blank 100 square.

✦ Plenary session

- ✦ Ask the children tell you how they split up their numbers, for example *"45 is 4 tens and 5 units and it looks like this on an abacus, and this is 45 in ten rods and units."*
- ✦ *"How did you know that number is 37? How many tens does it have? How many units? If it had one more unit, what number would it be then."*
- ✦ Group 3 children can explain how they found the position of numbers on the blank 100 square.

LESSON TWO
PIRATE PENNIES

✦ Assessment focus

Can the children understand grouping in 10s?

✦ Resources

- ✦ straws in bundles of tens and ones
- ✦ bags with 10 'sweets' in them and single 'sweets'
- ✦ number cards
- ✦ lots of pennies, 10 pence coins, pound coins

✦ Oral work and mental calculation

Number bonds to 20

- ✦ Make a set of cards with the numbers 0 to 20 on one side and the number that makes that number up to 20 on the other side (so 17 will have 3 on the reverse side). Hold up the cards in turn and ask the children to call out the number on the other side. Play it in the circle as well, for example put cards down randomly and ask a child to turn

over a 3. (So they have to choose the 17 card.) With a similar set of cards but up to 10, this can be a teacher independent game for children who need support with number bonds to 10.

✦ Starting point: whole class

- ✦ Go over doubles of numbers in preparation for the game later. Ask *"What is a quick way to count out a lot of coins or cubes?"* (Group them in twos or tens.) Count about 100 cubes grouped in tens.
- ✦ Use a large place value board and demonstrate how to play the pennies game, (see Activity sheet 1 on page 15) being sure to emphasise what happens when you need to exchange ten pennies for a ten pence piece, and that each throw of the dice means you win that many <u>pennies.</u>

£ pounds	10 ps	units
	⑩ ⑩	○○○ ○○

- ✦ Explain that some children will be playing the game slightly differently (groups 2 and 3) and they have to watch for any doubles thrown with the dice. They say 'double' then write down how

Place value and ordering

much money they have at that time, ready to show at the plenary session. Demonstrate this on the board.

✦ Emphasise the zero when we write multiples of 10, using the zero as a place holder.

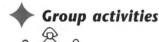

✦ Group activities

 Focus group

Each child needs an abacus or a hundreds, tens and units board and cubes or pennies. They count with you from about 7, adding on one cube or penny at a time so that when they come to 10, they will need to do some kind of exchange. *"When you have 10 pennies in the units column, you exchange them for one ten pence coin and put that in the tens column. Ten pence is one ten and no units."*

Continue to 20, then 30, observing carefully who can make the exchanges without prompting for multiples of ten. Explain that there isn't time to go on adding ones like this, so they must now make 98 on their abacus. Go on adding ones and ask *"Now what happens? We have 10 lots of 10."* Explain about moving into the hundreds column. *"We have one hundred, no tens and no units."*

 Teacher independent groups

Activity sheet 1: This is just the pennies game. The children need to play in pairs with two dice each. They take turns to throw both dice and take that many pennies. Encourage the partners to check the calculation. The pennies are placed in the pennies purse. When all the pennies are covered, they are exchanged for one ten pence coin and with the next throw of the dice, <u>pennies</u> are added. Beware that once children have one ten pence coin they are likely to add ten pence coins at the next throw rather than pennies. They are likely to need help to know how much money they end with.

Activity sheet 2: This is the pennies game with one difference. Every time anyone throws a double, each person has to add up how much money they have at that time and write it down. This will need careful follow up at review time particularly to teach how to write pounds and pennies.

Activity sheet 3: This is the same as Activity sheet 2 but it has an extra question for you to do with them at the plenary session. (See also chapter 10 lesson 2.)

✦ Plenary session

✦ Go over what exchanging means, and emphasise that we group in tens. Show how to write amounts of money correctly using the £. p notation.

✦ Groups 2 and 3 can demonstrate the amounts of money they had when a double was thrown.

✦ Further activities

✦ Use different layouts of numbers on a 100 square (generic sheet 2 on page 91), for example 0–99, or start with 1 at the bottom left.

✦ Demonstrate how a 100 square can be cut up to make a number line to make sure children understand the relationship between a number line and a 100 square.

✦ Extension

✦ Extend place value to thousands.

✦ Support

✦ Give a large handful of cubes to these children and ask them to count them, making 'ten trains' and units, then place their 'ten trains' on a place value board and circle their number on a 100 square.

✦ Pirate pennies ✦

✦ You need: 2 dice, lots of 1p, 10p and £1 coins.

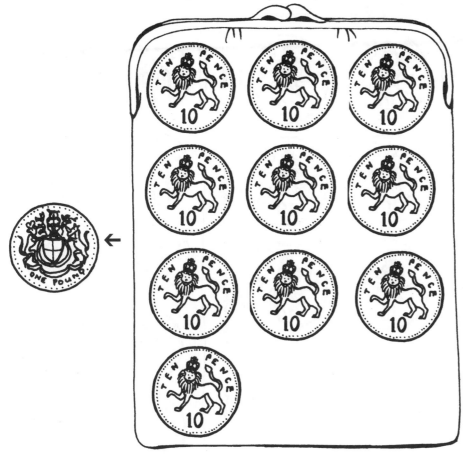

1. Throw both dice and add up all the dots.

2. Take that many pennies and put them in the penny purse.

3. Do exchanges as you go along.

4. The first to £1 is the winner.

I ended with £ ☐ ☐ 10s and ☐ 1s

📖 You have £10. What would you buy?

£6.50   £5.00   £7.99   £9.99   £4.99

✦ Pirate pennies ✦

✦ You need: 2 dice, lots of 1p, 10p and £1 coins.

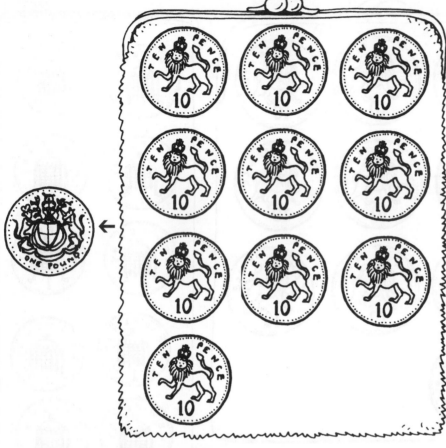

1. Throw both dice and add up all the dots.

2. Take that many pennies and put them in the penny purse.

3. Do exchanges as you go along.

4. The first to £1 is the winner.

5. When you throw a ⋛double⋚ write your total of money.

   1. _____   2. _____   3. _____   4. _____

I ended with **£** ☐   ☐ **10s** and ☐ **1s**

 You have £10. What would you buy?

◆ Pirate pennies ◆

◆ You need: 2 dice, lots of 1p, 10p and £1 coins.

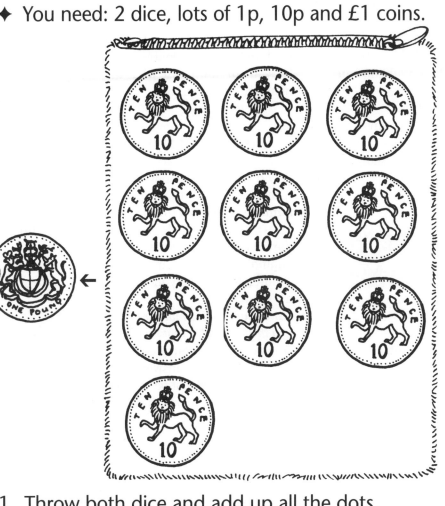

1. Throw both dice and add up all the dots.

2. Take that many pennies and put them in the penny purse.

3. Do exchanges as you go along.

4. The first to £1 is the winner.

5. When you throw a ⚡double⚡ write your total of money.

   1. _____   2. _____   3. _____   4. _____

I ended with £ _____

_____

   Write 123p in pounds   =   £ 1 . 2 3

Write 125p in pounds   =   £ ☐ . ☐ ☐

Write 250p in pounds   =   £ ☐ . ☐ ☐

developing
Numeracy
Skills

Photocopiable

17

Counting and patterns

 Overall learning objectives

✦ Investigate a general statement that doubling can be undone by halving.
✦ Describe and extend number sequences.
✦ Make links between operations of multiplying and dividing.
✦ Experience of checking calculations and asking if an answer is reasonable.
✦ Experience of 2 x, 5 x and 10 x tables.

**✦ LESSON ONE ✦
DOUBLING & HALVING**

 Assessment focus

Can the children talk about the general statement that when you double a number, then halve it again, you get back to the number you started with?

 Resources

✦ a set of digit cards 1–20
✦ cubes for each child
✦ large 100 square
✦ task cards (see below)

 Oral work and mental calculation

Doubling and halving

✦ Play 'are you my double?' Sit children in a circle and give out a shuffled set of cards 1–20 or above (some children can work in pairs). The children hold up their numbers, then the first child looks for the child with the number that is double their own and asks that person to come and sit next to them. *"My number is 4 and Ellie has double 4 – that is 8. Ellie please come and sit next to me."* At first, make just pairs of children, but later go for number sequences so 2, 4, 8, and 16 make a number chain, all of them sitting together.
✦ A much noisier version of the game is to give out the cards and let the children stand up and find

their double, then make their number chain. Explain that if 4 is double 2, then 2 is half of 4. Show them how to use what they know to add near doubles, such as 8 + 9.

 Starting point: whole class

✦ Play a halving and doubling circle game. Start with 10 different 'trains' of cubes (for example, numbers between 4 and 15) and give these out to pairs around the circle. They make another train the same size so that they now have double the original number. Go around the circle, with the children telling everyone the starting number and the double.
✦ *"Give your doubled number to the person next to you and they can halve your number. What happens?"* (You get back to your starting number.)
✦ Focus on expected answers. *"If someone said half of 20 was 80, would that be reasonable?"*, *"If we tried to guess the answer to half of 48, would it be closest to 20 or to 100?"*

 Group activities

 Focus group

Using a large hundred square, say the 5 and 10 times table. Give out multiples of 5 number cards and ask the children to double the numbers, recording what they do by drawing and writing. (You are looking for them to make multiples of 10.)

 Teacher independent groups

Group 1: Give out the number cards and let the children choose what, if any, apparatus they need to use to find doubles and/or halves of the numbers. They should record their findings in their own way.

Group 2: Give this group number cards for doubling or task cards, such as 'Crisps cost 17 pence a packet, so how much would two packets cost?' (Encourage the children to think of a double they do know, such as double 15, and think how they could use that to work out new doubles.)

18
©Hopscotch Educational Publishing

developing
**Numeracy
Skills**

**Numeracy
Year 2/P3**

Counting and patterns

Group 3: Give this group task cards, such as: 'Marbles cost 35p a bag, crisps 15p and apples 25p. How much would two bags of each cost?' and 'Tom has £1 and he spent half. How much did he spend?' Ask the children to make a guess first. *"Would you expect your answer to be about 50 pence or about £10? What could you do to check you are right?"*

✦ Plenary session

✦ Each group can demonstrate their work, explaining how they found halves and doubles. *"Tell us about halves of multiples of 10 and doubles of multiples of 5."*

✦ *"Double 10 is 20 and half of 20 is 10. What happens when you double a number and then halve it again?"*

✦ Keep stressing the need to look carefully at answers and ask if they are reasonable. *"Is that the kind of answer you were expecting?"*

LESSON TWO HIT 24

✦ Assessment focus

Can the children describe and extend number sequences?

✦ Resources

✦ large 100 square
✦ digit cards for 5 and 10 times table
✦ generic sheet 5 (page 94)
✦ operation cards ÷ and x and =

✦ Oral work and mental calculation

Addition and multiplication

✦ Play the 24s game. Write a square like this on the board, or put large pieces of paper with the numbers written on them on the floor.

4	2	1
24	3	8
6	0	12

✦ The children stand on the numbers (or Blu-tack counters on the numbers on the board) in turn and keep a running total to make 24, for example 12 + 8 + 4. Find different ways to do it, such as 12 + 6 + 2 + 4. Then play the game using multiplication. Two children stand on the numbers that total 24 such as 8 x 3, 4 x 6, 12 x 2, 24 x 1. Keep asking *"Is there another way to do it?"* Set various problems, such as *"What happens if we multiply by zero?"* (You get zero.) *"Are there 2 numbers next to each other that make 24 by multiplying?"*

✦ Starting point: whole class

✦ Play 'Hit 24'. You need a 100 square on display. Choose a number sequence, for example counting in 2s or counting in 5s, and ask if they will 'hit 24'. So, if you say all the even numbers, you will hit (land on) 24, but if you say the odd numbers or count in 10s from zero you won't. Encourage the children to predict and use multiplication tables, and to describe the pattern.

✦ Group activities

Focus group

✦ Continue the starter activity, asking children to tell you the rule for each sequence, for example 4, 8, 12. *"Tell me how you knew 16 was the next number*

Counting and patterns

in my pattern." You are looking for a description of the rule, such as 'It is counting in 4s'.

✦ Use more complex sequences to suit your groups. *"If we count in 3s starting at 2 will we hit 24?"* (No. 2, 5, 8, 11, 14, 17, 20, 23, 26)

✦ For those that can, extend the sequences on a 100 square (generic sheet 1 on page 90).

 Teacher independent groups

Use the photocopiable activity sheets

Activity sheet 1: These are simple sequences and no words need to be written. The children tick any 24s they get to. They should talk about the patterns they find. You might want to talk to them about the pattern they need to make up.

Activity sheet 2: These sequences don't start from zero. The children need to write a description of some sequences and make up their own.

Activity sheet 3: The first two sequences don't start from zero. The children have to make a pattern that doesn't hit 24 and another that does hit 24 and describe them.

 Plenary session

✦ Focus on the children's descriptions of their patterns. Ask how they knew when they would hit 24. Look for descriptions of odd number patterns, missing 24 and children saying that 24 is in some of the times tables.

✦ Ask the children what they have learned today about number patterns.

 Further activities

✦ Use generic sheet 5 (page 94) to make a doubling game, using the numbers 0–15 in the sack and doubles of all those in the coins. Use 'x 2' or 'double' on the sign post. The children choose a number from the sack, then

cover the double of that number on the coin grid. The first to get three in a row in any direction wins a gold coin.

✦ Try some more complex sequences, for example 1 (add 1), 2 (add 2), 4 (add 3), 7 and so on.

 Extension

✦ Using a shopping catalogue, (or prepared shopping cards) children choose items and find out how much two would cost. Extend to finding how much change there would be from £10/20.

 **Support**

✦ Find doubles of dominoes and work out totals.

✦ Using a 1–10 spinner, the children take turns to spin and find out the double of that number. They should record their findings in their own way.

◆ Hit 24 ◆

✦ Put a ✔ by the line of numbers that will hit 24.

2 4 6 8

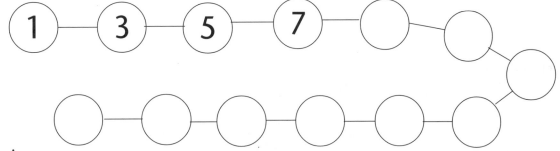

1 3 5 7

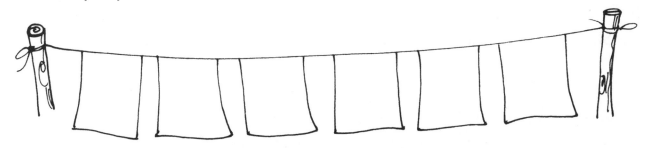

0 5 10 15

✦ Make up a pattern.

📖 Make up more patterns.

developing Numeracy Skills

21

✦ Hit 24 ✦

✦ Put a ✔ by the line of numbers that will hit 24 and a ✗ by those that won't.

1.

2.

9	11	13	15					

This pattern is _____

3.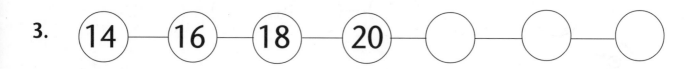

This pattern is _____

4. Start at ☐ 3 ☐ add **4** each time.

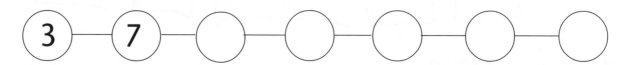

5. Start at ☐ add ☐ each time.

 Use a 100 square and make a pattern that hits 100.

Name _____

✦ Hit 24 ✦

✦ Put a ✔ by the line of numbers that will hit 24
and a ✗ by those that won't.

1. Start at 10. Count in 3s.

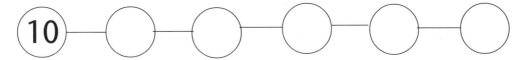

2. Start at 8. Count in 3s.

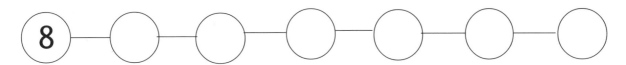

3. Start at 0. Count in 4s.

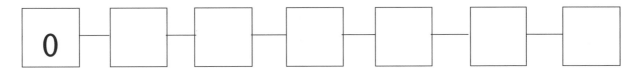

4. Make a pattern that misses 24.

My pattern is _____

5. Make a pattern that hits 24.

My pattern is _____

Use a 100 square and make a pattern that hits 100.

developing
Numeracy
Skills

Addition

 ### Overall learning objectives

- ✦ Use knowledge that addition can be done in any order to do mental calculations more efficiently.
- ✦ Put the larger number first when adding.
- ✦ Record calculations on a number line.
- ✦ Check calculations in a variety of ways, for example add in a different order.
- ✦ Begin to understand the link between addition and subtraction.

LESSON ONE
TWO-JUMP ADDING

 ### Assessment focus

Can the children partition numbers to aid addition calculations?

 ### Resources

- ✦ number lines
- ✦ generic sheet 3 (page 92)

 ### Oral work and mental calculation

Putting the larger number first

- ✦ Ask the children to add numbers such as 3 and 8 and then tell you how they did it. Draw their attention to how putting the 8 first and then counting on in 1s is quicker than counting all the way from 3. Praise those children who have other methods, such as 2 + 8 is 10, so 3 + 8 must be one more.

 ### Starting point: whole class

Before doing this lesson children need to have some experience of showing calculations on a number line.

- ✦ Explain that for this part of the lesson they do not need to put the larger number first; they are going

to split numbers and must always take two jumps on the number line each time. Demonstrate this with 4 + 11. *"You could do this by putting the larger number first then counting on, but you can also do it by splitting a number like this."*

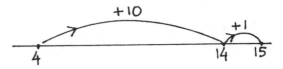

"4 + 10 is 14, so that is one jump of 10, plus one more is 15. That took 2 jumps to do the adding on."

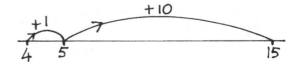

"Or you could make the 4 up to 5, then you have 10 more so that is 15."

- ✦ 6 + 20 could be done by splitting the 20 into 2 jumps of 10.
- ✦ 6 + 12 could be done by splitting the 12 into 6 and 6, so you take one jump of 6, then another of 6. Or you could make the first 6 up to 10 with a jump of 4 then add another 8.
- ✦ Say *"Sometimes you might wish that you could do 3 jumps, but you must try today to do them all with just 2. I will ask you at the end of this lesson where you think taking more than 2 jumps would have made it easier."* Give one more example and invite the children to suggest how this might be done.

 ### Group activities

Focus group

Give numbers that could be quite demanding for the children and ask them to find two different ways to do the calculations. One way is to do the two hops, but they must find another way as well. So, with 3 + 13, they must do the two hops, then tell you another way, such as putting the larger number first. Make sure that all the children are representing hops adequately on a number line. Note where children would like to take 3 jumps, for example when adding 30 by taking 3 jumps of 10.

Addition

 Teacher independent groups

Group 1: Provide a sheet of number lines with at least some of the numbers marked (see generic sheet 3.) Give additions for 2 jumps such as 5 + 6, 3 + 8, 8 + 11 and so on.

Group 2: Provide the number lines sheet and calculations such as 4 + 18, 7 + 9, 5 + 13 and so on.

Group 3: If these children are very experienced with a number line they could draw their own, or you could provide them with a sheet of calculations such as 11 + 19, 8 + 18, 7 + 21, 6 + 15, 9 + 23 and so on.

 Plenary session

✦ Each group should demonstrate their two hops on the board at the front. *"Can you think of another way you could have done that calculation?"*

✦ Ask the focus group children to show their other ways. Ask if anyone found a different way to split up their numbers, for example 13 + 26 split into tens and units.

✦ *"Tell me the times when you wanted to do more than 2 jumps to make it easier. When you are doing a calculation you won't have me saying it must be done with 2 jumps! In your head you can do as many jumps as you want, but don't go back to counting just in ones as you did when you were very young."*

LESSON TWO
ADD AND CHECK

 Assessment focus

Can the children check an addition sum in a variety of ways?

 Resources

✦ cubes, coins, yoghurt pots

 Oral work and mental calculation

Linking addition and subtraction

✦ Play 'Pete and Pam's treasure pot.' Pete and Pam have a pot of gold coins and they like to play games with them. They have 20 coins. (Put 20 cubes or coins in a pot so that the children can't see them.) *"Pete has brought out 10 of the coins, so how many are left in the pot?"* Repeat this several times, bringing out different numbers of coins. Give experience with empty box equations, for

example *"20 coins altogether and 3 are out. That leaves how many in the pot? Something and 3 makes 20."* Write that on the board as ☐ + 3 = 20.

✦ Vary the equations as much as possible, for example:

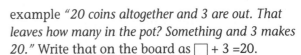

$$20 - \square = 17$$
$$17 + 3 = 19 + \square$$

 Starting point: whole class

The children need to have experience of jumps on a number line both forward and back for this lesson.

✦ *"What is 4 and 5 more? How can you check if 9 is right?"* Let the children show you their checking methods – counting on fingers and so on. Then teach them two checking methods: doing the addition in a different order, 5 + 4, (so if they get the same answer, that is one way to check); and undoing the addition by doing a subtraction, so 4 + 5 is 9. 9 – 5 you get back to the 4 again. Demonstrate the arrow on the activity sheets that indicates where a calculation is to be reversed.

Addition

✦ Focus on doing a subtraction to undo an addition and demonstrate this on a number line with 'round and rounds'. Use the number lines on generic sheet 4 on page 93 to show more 'round and rounds' on number lines to consolidate the relationship between addition and subtraction.

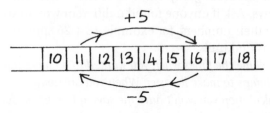

"11 + 5 is 16. To check that calculation, jump back 5 and you get back to 11 again."

 Group activities

 Focus group

Explore checking methods, especially doing the addition in a different order and checking addition by doing the related subtraction. Give the children experience of working with numbers up to and beyond 20, for example 13 + 4, 15 + 3, 7 + 9, 8 + 11, 12 + 7, 12 + 30, 18 + 50. More able children can be given 12 + 17, 13 + 19, 14 + 17.

 Teacher independent groups

Use the photocopiable activity sheets

Activity sheet 1: This sheet is laid out with the two checking methods in the starter, reversing the order and using subtraction. For those who find choosing their own numbers hard you could provide number cards or two 0–9 dice. Offer a selection of apparatus, such as number lines and let the children choose, but ask *"Can you do that in your head?"*

Activity sheet 2: This uses slightly harder calculations. You could suggest that these children try to do it without cubes, but work mentally or use a number line.

Activity sheet 3: Suggest that these children draw their own number lines on the sheet and show hops back and forward as a way of checking.

 Plenary session

✦ The groups should demonstrate their checking by undoing addition with subtraction. Say *"Tell me why that works."* and ask *"What is the opposite of addition?"* (Subtraction.)
✦ Stress that they must always check calculations. *"Tell me one way you can do checking? ... and another way?"*
✦ *"What did you learn today?"*

 Further activities

✦ Check calculations by using numbers you know. To add 7 and 12, we know 7 + 10 is 17, so 7 + 12 will be 2 more, 19.
✦ Use generic sheet 4 (page 93) to give more experience in the relationship between addition and subtraction.

 Extension

✦ Let children explore calculations of two-digit numbers and with numbers beyond 100.

 Support

✦ Let children play dice and spinner games, adding two numbers together mentally.
✦ Use generic sheet 5 (page 94) to make more simple three-in-a-row mental maths games. The children play in pairs and take turns to add a number from the sack to a number on the sign post and cover their answer with their colour counter. The first to get three in a row in any direction is the winner.

✦ Add and check ✦

✦ **Add.**   ✦ **Now check.**

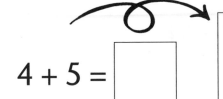

$4 + 5 =$ ☐

Check 1

$5 + 4 =$ ☐

Check 2

$9 - 4 =$ ☐

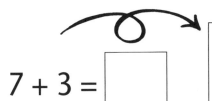

$7 + 3 =$ ☐

Check 1

$3 + 7 =$ ☐

Check 2

$10 - 7 =$ ☐

$6 + 3 =$ ☐

Check 1

$3 + 6 =$ ☐

Check 2

$9 - 6 =$ ☐

✦ Choose your own numbers to add and check.

Check 1   **Check 2**

Check 1   **Check 2**

 Add 17 and 3. Now check it.

Numeracy
Year 2/P3

developing
Numeracy Skills

Photocopiable
©Hopscotch Educational Publishing   27

✦ **Add and check** ✦

✦ Add.   ✦ Now check.

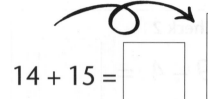

$14 + 15 =$ ☐

Check 1
$15 + 14 =$ ☐

Check 2
☐ $- 14 =$ ☐

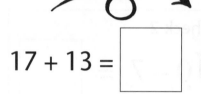

$17 + 13 =$ ☐

Check 1
$13 + 17 =$ ☐

Check 2
☐ $- 17 =$ ☐

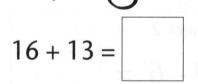

$16 + 13 =$ ☐

Check 1
$13 + 16 =$ ☐

Check 2
☐ $- 16 =$ ☐

✦ Use cards.

☐ $+$ ☐ $=$ ☐

Check 1

Check 2

☐ $+$ ☐ $=$ ☐

Check 1

Check 2

📖 Add 17 and 23. Now check it.

Photocopiable
©Hopscotch Educational Publishing

developing **Numeracy Skills**

Name _____

✦ Add and check ✦

✦ Add.   ✦ Now check 2 ways.

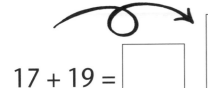

17 + 19 = ☐

Check 1	Check 2

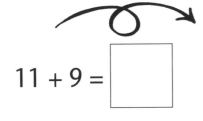

11 + 9 = ☐

Check 1	Check 2

✦ Now do your own using cards ☐15☐ to ☐35☐ . Always check two ways.

☐ + ☐ = ☐

Check 1	Check 2

☐ + ☐ = ☐

Check 1	Check 2

☐ + ☐ = ☐

Check 1	Check 2

📖 Add 117 and 23. Now check it.

developing
Numeracy Skills

Subtraction

 ### Overall learning objectives

- ✦ Use the vocabulary of subtraction and addition and make related number sentences in a variety of formats.
- ✦ Partition numbers to aid mental calculations.
- ✦ Know all subtraction (and addition) facts that make 20.
- ✦ Find a small difference by counting up.
- ✦ Represent subtractions on a number line.

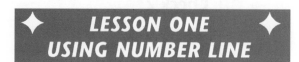

**LESSON ONE
USING NUMBER LINE**

 ### Assessment focus

Can the children partition numbers to aid subtraction calculations?

 ### Resources

- ✦ generic sheet 3 (page 92)
- ✦ number lines

 ### Oral work and mental calculation

Finding a small difference by counting up

- ✦ Demonstrate to the children how to find a small difference, such as between 9 and 11, by starting at the lower number and counting up on your fingers. (This is a good time to count in 1s, but you wouldn't find the difference between 54 and 7 this way!) Say *"Show me how to find the difference between 8 and 13 by counting up … it is much quicker than counting back."* You could demonstrate each of the calculations on a number line on the board.

 ### Starting point: whole class

- ✦ (You can do this lesson over several days.) Demonstrate simple subtractions on a number

line, for example 23 – 10 and others where taking jumps of 10 is relevant.

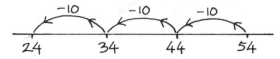

"To do 54 – 30 you can jump back in steps of 10."

- ✦ If the children need experience of counting back in steps of 10, use generic sheet 3 (page 92) to practise this.
- ✦ When they are secure with multiples of 10, move on to taking away single-digit numbers from multiples of 10, such as 40 – 3, 18 – 5 and 19 – 7.
- ✦ Move to taking a 'teens' number from a 2-digit number without crossing the tens boundary, for example 27 – 13, 68 – 14 and 37 – 15.
- ✦ Move on to splitting numbers by taking 2 jumps back each time, choosing suitable numbers, such as a single digit from a 'teens' number.

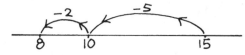

"15 – 7 can be done as 15 – 5 – 2. You can make the numbers easier by jumping back 5 first to make 10, then another 2."

- ✦ Show group 3 children how to do their activity.

 ### Group activities

 Focus group

Assess who is able to split single-digit numbers appropriately to make numbers easier and who is able to explain what they have done and why. Some children may be able to subtract a single-digit number from a 'twenties' number, crossing the 20 as a middle stage (see the group 3 activity).

Teacher independent groups

Group 1: Use generic sheet 3 with simple subtractions below 20 that can be done in 2 jumps, such as 11 – 5, (count back 1 to 10, then another 4).

Subtraction

The children might choose a variety of ways to split their numbers, although you need to emphasise that they must not count back in steps of one. This might be too hard for some and they might need cubes to count in ones.

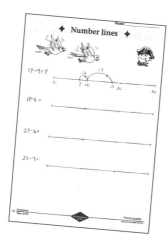

To make it more straightforward you could keep each calculation on each sheet with the same numbering on the empty number lines.

Group 2: Focus these children on to thinking very carefully about the two jumps they make, so making the numbers easier, for example 17 – 9 = 17 – 5 – 4 and 18 – 6 (jump 3 to 15, then jump 3).

Group 3: Ask these children to subtract a single-digit number from a 'twenties' number, crossing 20 as a middle stage, such as 23 – 7 = 23 – 3 – 4, and 27 – 9 = 27 – 7 – 2.

◆ *Plenary session*

- ✦ Let each group explain their two jumps. Emphasise how the jumps make the numbers easier, for example splitting the 7 in 15 – 7 into a jump of 5 to get to 10 and then 2 more. *"We must remember that splitting up numbers can often make a calculation easier to do in our head."*
- ✦ *"Who can tell me a different way to do this one?"* Let the children explore a range of ways to calculate and make the point that counting back in ones is very slow.
- ✦ *"Close your eyes. Make a picture of a number line. Put 19 on your number line and take away 7 in two jumps."*

◆ ◆ ◆ ◆ ◆ ◆ ◆ ◆ ◆ ◆ ◆ ◆ ◆

◆ LESSON TWO YOU KNOW ...

◆ *Assessment focus*

Can the children use the vocabulary of subtraction and addition and say and write subtraction facts and corresponding addition facts?

◆ *Resources*

- ✦ Blu-tack
- ✦ number words cards, such as 'add' and 'plus'

◆ *Oral work and mental calculation*

Making connections

- ✦ Explore a wide range of the language of calculating, such as '3 plus 8 equals 11', 'the difference between 11 and 8 is 3', demonstrating how knowing one number fact means that others can be known as well.
- ✦ *"17 + 3 makes 20, 3 + 17 is 20 as well, so we can work out that 20 – 17 is 3 and 20 minus 3 leaves 17."*

◆ *Starting point: whole class*

- ✦ On the board display a number sentence, such as 10 – 7 = 3 and ask how that could be written another way, using the same 3 numbers, but ending up with a different number sentence.
- ✦ Establish that because you know 10 – 7 = 3, you can work out that 10 – 3 = 7 and you also know

Numeracy
Year 2/P3

developing
Numeracy
Skills

31

©Hopscotch Educational Publishing

Subtraction

that 3 + 7 = 10 and 7 + 3 = 10. Demonstrate this on a number line as on Activity sheet 2.

✦ Do another few examples using the number bonds to 10 so that all children might be able to understand the lesson and enabling group 1 children to understand their activity.
10 – 6 = 4   10 – 4 = 6   4 + 6 = 10   6 + 4 = 10

✦ You can do this with fingers, but try to move the children on to thinking about numbers mentally.

Group activities

 Focus group

Use Blu-tack and number cards to make related number sentences for review time. You could include word cards as well, for example 'plus' and 'subtract', if these children seem to need help relating the vocabulary to the symbols. Use challenging numbers for some, such as 24 – 13 = 11 and make sure that they can all read a number sentence with a missing number, such as 24 – ☐ = 11 as '24 take away something leaves 11' and give a variety of words for the = symbol, such as 'balances' and 'makes' and 'equals'.

 Teacher independent groups

Use the photocopiable activity sheets

Activity sheet 1: These children should make four related number sentences in each section. It would help to have the starter calculations left on display.

Activity sheet 2: This sheet uses the number bonds of 20.

Activity sheet 3: Let these children choose their three related numbers, such as 15, 6 and 21.

Plenary session

✦ Make links between the numbers on Activity sheets 1 and 2 (10 – 6 and 20 – 6).

✦ Check that the children can read their number sentences with appropriate vocabulary for the symbols.

✦ *"So, if you know 10 – 8 is 2, what else can you know just with those numbers?"*

Further activities

✦ Give repeated experience with pairs of numbers totalling 20. (See the oral maths starter in Chapter 2, Lesson Two)

✦ Keep emphasising the link between addition and subtraction. You can use generic sheet 4 (page 93), photocopying the bottom half of the sheet twice and sticking them together to make a sheet of blanks.

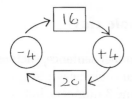 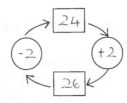

Extension

✦ Give experience of fairly complex subtractions that can be done by making jottings on a number line, such as 34 – 16.

Support

✦ Make sure that the children can use a wide range of language to talk about their calculations and that they can start to explain to you what they are doing in their head when calculating mentally. This can take some time to establish, but it is crucial that children feel that they can do some mental maths, so build up self-esteem. Make short-term achievable targets for the child and be lavish with praise.

---

developing
Numeracy
Skills

◆ Number sentences ◆

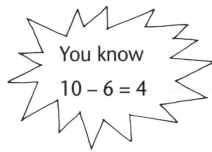

You know

10 − 6 = 4

so 10 − 4 = ⬜   and

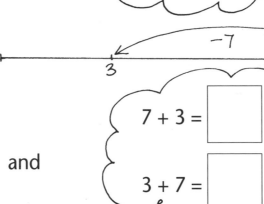

4 + 6 = ⬜

6 + 4 = ⬜

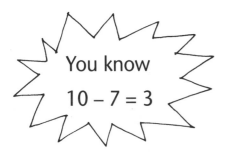

You know

10 − 7 = 3

so 10 − 3 = ⬜   and

7 + 3 = ⬜

3 + 7 = ⬜

Now do it with

10 − 1 = 9

10 − 9 = ⬜

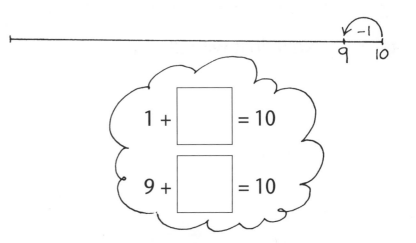

1 + ⬜ = 10

9 + ⬜ = 10

 Now do another split of 10.

5 + 5 = 10   8 + 2 = ⬜

developing
Numeracy
Skills

◆ Number sentences ◆

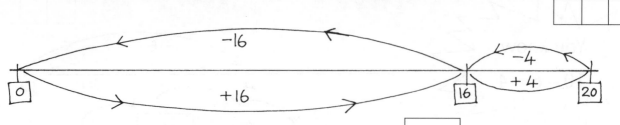

20 − 4 = 16   16 + ⬚ = 20

20 − 16 = ⬚   4 + ⬚ = 20

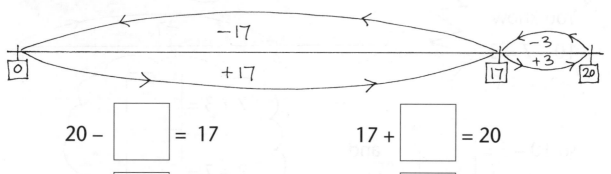

20 − ⬚ = 17   17 + ⬚ = 20

20 − ⬚ = 3   3 + ⬚ = 20

 Now do it with 20 − 1

 Now do another split of 20.

5 + 15 = 20   18 + ⬚ = 20

✦ Make 4 number sentences ✦

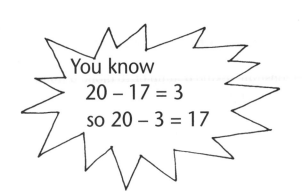

You know
20 – 17 = 3
so 20 – 3 = 17

and

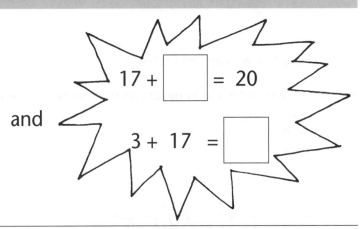

17 + ☐ = 20

3 + 17 = ☐

Choose another 3 numbers.

I chose ☐ and ☐ and ☐

Make 4 number sentences.

☐ – ☐ = ☐   ☐ + ☐ = ☐

☐ – ☐ = ☐   ☐ + ☐ = ☐

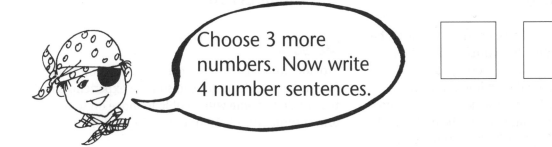

Choose 3 more numbers. Now write 4 number sentences.

☐ ☐ ☐

 ☐ – ☐ = 4

Calculation strategies – 1

 ## Overall learning objectives

✦ Add and subtract 9 and 11 by adding/subtracting 10 and adjusting.
✦ Use knowledge that addition can be done in any order to do mental calculations more efficiently.
✦ Partition numbers into 5 and a bit.

 ## LESSON ONE
HOW MANY?

 ## Assessment focus

Can the children add and subtract 9 and 11 by adding/subtracting 10 and adjusting?

Resources

✦ number cards
✦ number lines
✦ generic sheet 3 (page 92)

Oral work and mental calculation

Adding 3 small numbers

✦ Play 'Three card wizz.' Three children stand at the front of the class with a few cards behind their backs. On the count of 3, they bring out one card each and the others do the addition quickly and call out the answer. Extend the game to show how sometimes two of the numbers can be added first. For example, with 3 + 11 + 7, the 3 and 7 can be added first to make 10. You can do this by giving cards to the two children on the outside and letting the middle child hold up any number.

First add the 5 and 5 to make 10, then add on the 19.

Starting point: whole class

✦ Demonstrate taking a jump of 10 along a number line and jumping back one.

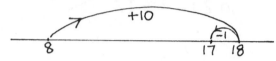

8 add 9 is 17 because 8 add 10 is 18, subtract 1 is 17.

✦ Remind the children that 9 is 1 less than 10 and give plenty of practice with this, the children coming to the front and drawing the jump of 10 and back 1.
✦ *"So, if you can add 9 in that quick way, can you think of a quick way to do 17 take away 9 on the number line?"* (You might perfer to leave this for another day.)

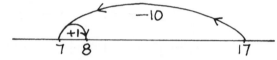

17 minus 9 is 8 because 17 - 10 is 7 add one more is 8.

✦ *"Shut your eyes and do these on the number line in your head. 13 – 9, 16 – 9, 21 – 9."*

Group activities

 Focus group

Provide number lines (see generic sheet 3 on page 92) and give calculations to suit the experiences of the children. Some will be able to move on to adding and subtracting 11, 19 and 21 using a similar method.

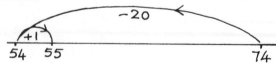

You can do 74 subtract 19 by first subtracting 20 then adding on the one.

Give the children experience of working without number lines and responding just to oral questions, such as 26 – 9, 35 – 9 and 87 – 19.

Calculation strategies – 1

Teacher independent groups

Group 1: These children should use generic sheet 3 (page 92) to add 9 to numbers up to 10 or 20.

Group 2: These children should use generic sheet 3 to add and subtract 9 and 11 to and from 'teen' and 'twenties' numbers, for example 15 + 9 and 27 – 11.

Group 3: These children could draw their own number lines to do a variety of calculations adding and subtracting 9, 11, (then later 19 and 21) to any 2- digit numbers.

◆ LESSON TWO 5 AND A BIT

◆ Assessment focus

Can the children partition into 5 and a bit when adding, then recombine?

◆ Resources

- abacuses, ten rods and units, cubes

◆ Oral work and mental calculation

Partitioning into tens and units

- Use Dienes apparatus and/or an abacus to remind children that we can split up numbers in a variety of ways. 14 is one ten and four ones, for example. Give the children a variety of 2-digit numbers, such as 16, 23, 76, 91 and 39, and ask them to split them mentally into tens and units.

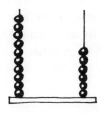

◆ Plenary session

- Let each group talk about their work, encouraging a wide range of words for addition and subtraction. *"Tell me another way to say that number sentence."*
- *"Who thinks they have learned another quick way to do adding today?"* Stress that it is much quicker to add 9 this way and not to count on in 1s on their fingers.

◆ Starting point: whole class

- Explain that today you are going to look at another way to split numbers to help with calculating. Do some finger counting of 5 and a bit keeping one hand as 5 all the time.
- Do several additions, each one starting with 5, for example 5 + 8, 5 + 6 and 5 + 9, and demonstrate how the second number can be split into 5 and a bit to make adding easier.

5 + 8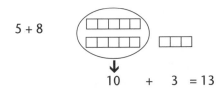

To do 5 plus 8, split the 8 into 5 + 3, then put the two fives together to make 10, then add the 3.

- Move on to needing to split up both numbers into 5 and a bit, for example 7+9.

7 + 9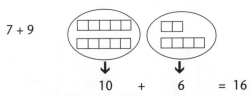

7 + 9 is (5 + 2) + (5 + 4). Combine the 5s to make 10. Then add the 2 and 4 to make 6. 10 + 6 = 16.

Calculation strategies – 1

+ Play 'finger wizz' with two children on the count of 3 bringing out both their hands with their choice of fingers up, but one hand must always be 5. Add the 2 numbers of fingers by adding both the 5s first.
+ Show how with larger numbers you can split into 15 and a bit, such as 17 + 8 can be 15 + 2 + 5 + 3.

Group activities

 Focus group

Ask children to explain what they are doing as they split into 5 and bit. Some children might need to use Unifix to split numbers and have more experience with understanding 6, 7, 8 and 9 as 5 and a bit, (see the fingers on activity sheet 1).

Further activities

+ Do other splitting into tens and units when that can make calculations easier (13 + 11).
+ Use generic sheet 6 (page 95) to do an adding game. Mark the four faces of a Unifix cube with 6, 7, 8, and 9. The children go different ways from the ship to the treasure chest. They take turns to throw the cube and add that number to the number in their next box. The partner must check what they do very carefully. If it is correct they make a move. If they are not correct, no move can be made.

 Teacher independent groups

Use the photocopiable activity sheets.

Activity sheet 1: Encourage these children to try to make pictures of the fingers in their head. All of the calculations just split the second number.

Activity sheet 2: These children need to split both numbers into 5 and a bit, then recombine the two 5s to make 10 and add on the other numbers.

Activity sheet 3: This sheet is more complex, with splitting both numbers, including splitting into 15 and a bit.

Plenary session

+ Let the children explain what they have done. Ask them to make their explanations very clear and to tell you the kinds of number that need to be split into 5 and a bit.
+ Play 'finger wizz' again.
+ *"What did you learn today about a quick way to do adding?"*

Extension

+ Ask the children to split calculations such as 27 + 8 into 25 and a bit.
+ Extend the game on generic sheet 6 to adding higher numbers.

Support

+ Give small groups practice in splitting numbers into 5 and bit, as on Activity sheet 2. Do it with fingers and two colours of cubes until the children can do it mentally. You could make some flash cards for number bonds of 5 and a bit, putting the answer on the back so that it is a self-checking, teacher-independent activity.
+ Use generic sheet 6 to make an easier adding game, just adding 5 each time.

◆ 5 and a bit ◆

5 add 7

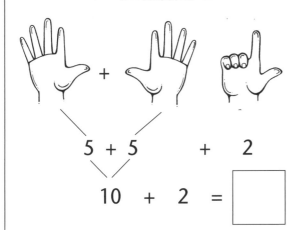

5 + 5   +   2

10   +   2   =   ☐

5 and 9

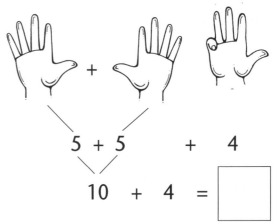

5 + 5   +   4

10   +   4   =   ☐

5 plus 6

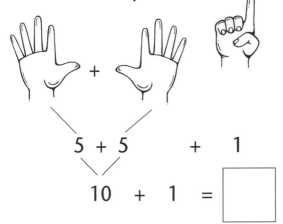

5 + 5   +   1

10   +   1   =   ☐

5 add 8 more

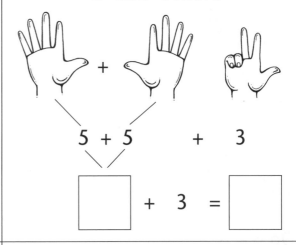

5 + 5   +   3

☐   +   3   =   ☐

5 + 5   +   5

☐   +   5   =   ☐

5 + 5   +   6

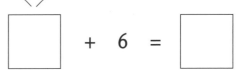

☐   +   6   =   ☐

 Throw 2 dice.

Make lots of sums.

✦ 5 and a bit ✦

6 add 7

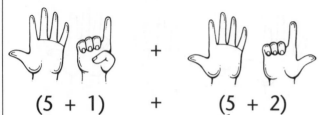

$(5 + 1)$ + $(5 + 2)$

10 + 1 + 2 = ☐

8 plus 7

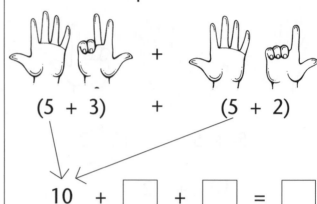

$(5 + 3)$ + $(5 + 2)$

10 + ☐ + ☐ = ☐

6 plus 9

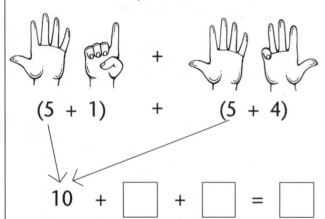

$(5 + 1)$ + $(5 + 4)$

10 + ☐ + ☐ = ☐

Do 9 + 7

Do 6 + 8

Do 8 + 9

📖 Do finger wizz with a partner. Write down your sums.

$5 + 2 + 5 + 4$

Photocopiable

Name _____

◆ 5 and a bit ◆

9 plus 8	8 + 7

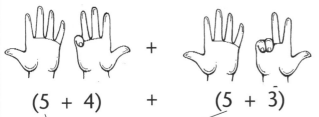

(5 + 4)　　　+　　　(5 + 3)

10　+　4 + 3　=　☐

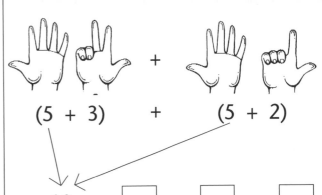

(5 + 3)　　　+　　　(5 + 2)

10　+　☐　+　☐　=　☐

Now split into 15 and a bit.

16 plus 7	17 + 8

(15 + 1)　　+　　(5 + 2)

20　+　☐　+　☐　=　☐

17 + 11	17 + 14

 Use cards ☐11☐ to ☐40☐ . Do adding by splitting.

Photocopiable
©Hopscotch Educational Publishing

developing
Numeracy
Skills

Calculation strategies – 2

 Overall learning objectives

✦ Use the knowledge that addition can be done in any order to do mental calculations efficiently.
✦ Choose appropriate ways of calculating a variety of numbers.
✦ Explain methods and reasoning orally.

LESSON ONE
THREE NUMBER ADDING

 Assessment focus

Can the children use their knowledge that numbers can be added in any order to add three numbers efficiently?

 Oral work and mental calculation

Number bonds to 10 (then 15 then 20)

✦ Play 'Ping pong to 10'. You say 'ping' and the class reply 'pong'. You say a number such as '7' and the class reply '3' to make the 7 up to 10. Play as a whole class, sometimes with the children coming out to the front to lead. Saying 'ping' (and they respond 'pong') every now and then between the numbers keeps their attention.

 Starting point: whole class

✦ (See also 'Three card wizz' Chapter 6 Lesson One.) Demonstrate how, when you are adding, you can often make pairs of numbers adding up to 10. For example, with 3 + 6 + 7, you can first add the 3 + 7 to make 10 then just add on the 6. Do several examples showing children how they can record the tens they find by linking them together with a line, as on the activity sheets.
✦ Include examples using large numbers and remind the children that to speed up calculations they can put the larger number first. Move on to much larger numbers, such as 1 + 9 + 51. Put the 51 in your head, then jump on 10 to 61.

 Group activities

 Focus group

Do some assessment of the children's calculating abilities, choosing numbers suitable for their experience. Able children will need to have experience of adding two-digit numbers so you could ask them to do 13 + 7 + 35, 18 + 2 + 49, indicating to them that they can put the larger number first and still find pairs of numbers that add to 10, or 20, or 30.

 Teacher independent groups

Use the photocopiable activity sheets

Activity sheet 1: This sheet starts with finding numbers that make up to 10, then the third number is added. The second section asks the children to put the larger number first then add on. The arrow with the loop is used again to indicate reversing the numbers.

Activity sheet 2: This has the same two sections as Activity sheet 1, but the numbers are larger and there is less support for putting the largest number first.

Activity sheet 3: This is a selection of calculations that can be done in a variety of ways. In the lower section the children should show how they did the calculations.

 Plenary session

✦ Focus on thinking about ways that the children can add together three numbers.
✦ Let each group say what they did. Write on the board some of the ways they chose. Make a display of this both for the mental maths sessions for a few days and to help with Lesson Two.
✦ Ask *"Why do we put the larger number first when we add?"* (It can make you quicker.)
✦ *"Try to remember that there is always more than one way to do a calculation and you need to look carefully at the numbers before you decide what you will do."*

Calculation strategies – 2

LESSON TWO
IN YOUR HEAD

Assessment focus

Can the children choose from a range of ways of calculating and explain methods?

Resources

✦ number cards

Oral work and mental calculation

Addition of 2-digit numbers

✦ Play 'Two card wizz'. Introduce the game by adding and subtracting 10 to any 2-digit number. Then show how to add 9 by adding 10 and hopping back one on the number line. Play the game with two sets of cards, one 1–100, the other (at first) just the cards 9, 19, 11 and 21.

✦ Two children come out to the front and each holds about five cards behind their back (use numbers to suit your children). On the count of 3, they each bring out one of their cards and the rest of the children have to add the two numbers mentally and call out the total, or hold up digit cards. Talk about the mental strategies they used.

✦ Develop the game to doing subtraction.

Starting point: whole class

✦ Explain that this lesson is about looking at lots of different calculations and deciding how best to do them. Explain how it is very important to look very carefully at the numbers before you decide how you will do the sum.

✦ "So, you wouldn't do 5 + 9 by near doubling. How could you do it?"

✦ "Now look at these numbers very carefully and tell me how you would do them." Write on the board something that is an obvious near double, such as 8+7, and something like 12 + 9, reminding the

children that they know a quick number line jumping method for adding 9. Ask them to tell you _how_ you could do those two sums – not asking for the answer yet. Demonstrate the methods that the children suggest.

✦ "Now someone tell us some more numbers that we could add by near doubles, adding 9 by adding 10 and taking 1 away and so on."

Group activities

Focus group

(This activity needs a long plenary session, so keep the group work fairly short.) Use this time to help children who are struggling with one or more of the mental calculations strategies. It can help to ask children to record their work on number lines or to draw pictures of what they do.

Teacher independent groups

Group 1: Give more practice with calculating strategies that the group or individuals need help with, such as adding three small numbers. You could make number wheels or give them shuffled cards or spinners and let them record their work in their own way.

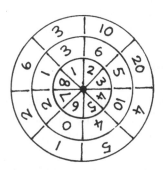

A number wheel made with a split pin and a series of cards that can be rotated.

Group 2: Some children might be able to do Activity 3 sheet from Lesson One. Others can do what group 1 are doing but using larger numbers.

Calculation strategies – 2

Group 3: Give these children a selection of calculations on slips of paper including calculations that can be done by near doubling, adding 9 and 11 by adding 10 and adjusting, finding pairs to make 10 and so on. Ask the children to sort them into types, sticking them down with Blu-tack.

 Plenary session

✦ You won't have time to go through every calculation, but give some children time to explain their work, observing carefully who can explain what they have done well.

✦ Show the children's own recordings and let group 3 show their different types of calculations. Use these sets to get other groups to find a calculation that they did in a similar way. Make a display of this work.

You could do these putting the larger number first then adding on.

2 + 84   4 + 17   1 + 2 + 51

You could do these by first making 20, then adding on.

3 + 16 + 17   1 + 54 + 19

Do these by adding near doubles.

50 + 51   18 + 17   25 + 26

✦ *"What did you learn today about deciding which way you will do a calculation?"* (Hopefully someone will say you need to look carefully at numbers first.)

 Further activities

✦ Repeat each different strategy one at a time in mental maths time for several weeks and keep a display going so that children learn to think of doing calculations in several different ways.

Extension

✦ Give some 'real' numbers to add, such as till receipts from shops. The children could use a shopping catalogue to add up the cost of three or four items.

✦ Challenge them to make a difficult adding or subtracting game, using a blank copy of generic sheet 5 (page 94).

Support

✦ If these children need more work adding small numbers mentally, make a game on generic

sheet 6 (page 95) putting quite small numbers in the spaces. In pairs, the children take turns to throw two dice and add the numbers to the number in the space they are on and say the total. If they are right, they move on one space.

✦ Find the hidden 10s ✦

$5 + 4 + 5$

$10 + 4 = \boxed{}$

$7 + 6 + 3$

$\boxed{} + \boxed{6} = \boxed{}$

$9 + 5 + 1$

$10 + 5 = \boxed{}$

$8 + 7 + 2$

$\boxed{10} + \boxed{} = \boxed{}$

$5 + 8 + 5$

$\boxed{} + \boxed{} = \boxed{}$

$6 + 8 + 4$

✦ Now put the larger number first

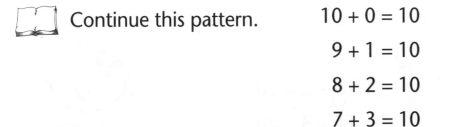

$3 + 7 + 11$ ⟳ $11 +$

$6 + 4 + 13$ ⟳ $13 +$

📖 Continue this pattern.

$10 + 0 = 10$

$9 + 1 = 10$

$8 + 2 = 10$

$7 + 3 = 10$

developing
Numeracy
Skills

✦ **Find the hidden 10s** ✦

7 + 16 + 3

10 + 16 = ☐

5 + 17 + 5

☐ + 17 = ☐

8 + 14 + 2

10 + ☐ = ☐

6 + 18 + 4

10 + ☐ = ☐

✦ Now put the largest number first.

6 + 4 + 13   13 +

7 + 21 + 3   ☐ +

4 + 29 + 6

5 + 31 + 5

4 + 35 + 6

 Continue this pattern.

20 + 0 = 20

19 + 1 = 20

18 + 2 = 20

17 + 3 = 20

developing
Numeracy
Skills

✦ Hidden numbers ✦

✦ Find the hidden 10s.

5 + 17 + 5

[ ] + 17 = [ ]

4 + 26 + 6

[ ] + 26 = [ ]

✦ Now find the hidden 20s.

15 + 39 + 5

20 + [ ] = [ ]

17 + 21 + 3

[ ] + 21 = [ ]

✦ Choose how you do these. Show how you did them.

3 + 4 + 17

3 + 7 + 41

15 + 16 + 1

21 + 37

 Use cards [20] – [50] and do some adding.

developing
Numeracy
Skills

Multiplication and division

✦ Overall learning objectives

✦ Begin to see that multiplication can be done in any order.
✦ Understand multiplication as repeated addition and an array of rows and columns.
✦ Understand how to make equal groupings.
✦ Use the language of 'lots of', times and sharing/grouping.

✦ LESSON ONE
CHANGE IT AROUND

✦ Assessment focus

Can the children understand how to make equal groupings and use the language of 'lots of'?

✦ Resources

✦ cubes
✦ trays
✦ generic sheet 2 (page 91)

✦ Oral work and mental calculation

Making 'lots of'

✦ Play 'Change it around'. Give each child 12 jewels (cubes) and all work together to make 3 lots of 4. The children should describe their groups, for example '3 lots of 4' or '4 + 4 + 4'. Then change it around to make 4 lots of 3. Make the point that there are still 12 cubes, but this time they are in 4 groups. Say 'change it around' again and children must go back to 3 lots of 4. Draw the groups on the board. Stress that 4 times 3 and 3 times 4 make the same number. Multiplication is a bit like addition – you can do it in any order. (You can also play the game by putting 12 cubes on one or more trays and passing these round the circle, for example 'make 2 groups of 6'.)

✦ Starting point: whole class

(See also Chapter 3.)
✦ Move on from the starter, this time relating 'lots of' to multiple addition. Each child uses 14 cubes and makes 7 lots of 2. Show how this can be written 2 + 2 + 2 + 2 + 2 + 2 + 2, but a quick way is 7 lots of 2 or 7 x 2 (or 2 x 7). Change it around to 2 lots of 7. Then make other 'lots of' with different numbers, stressing that you must always make equal groups, and each time demonstrating the multiple addition and the quick way to write it. Use the term 'multiplied by' and then finish the session with using 12 cubes so that group 1 know what to do.

✦ Group activities

Focus group

Use generic sheet 2 (page 91) to make arrays of cubes and ask the children to describe them. They can colour in and cut out their rectangles for display.

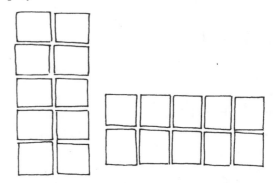

"I've made 5 rows of 2 in each row and I can change it around to 2 rows of 5 in each row."

Teacher independent groups

Use the photocopiable activity sheets

Activity sheet 1: The children doing this sheet just use 12 cubes each time to draw equal groups. Stress that they must make equal groups each time and make sure they can use the language of 'lots of'. The multiplication sign isn't used.

Multiplication and division

Activity sheet 2: These children start with 16, drawing equal groups, then do the multiple addition and the multiplication.

Activity sheet 3: Use this generic sheet for numbers to suit your children, for example starting with 24 jewels. There is space on the line with additions to add more numbers.

◆ ◆ ◆ ◆ ◆ ◆ ◆

◆ LESSON TWO
SHARE THE TREASURE ◆

◆ Assessment focus

Can the children understand equal grouping and use the language of sharing?

◆ Resources

+ cubes
+ margarine pots
+ spinners and dice
+ number cards
+ Blu-tack

◆ Oral work and mental calculation

Relating multiplication and division

+ Use fairly small numbers so that all the children can follow and choose a simple multiplication that they know, such as 3 x 2 = 6. Write it up on the board and ask them if they can make a division sentence with those numbers, for example '6 jewels shared between 2 pirates is 3 jewels each'. Can they make another sentence, again using just those three numbers?
+ Use Blu-Tack to display some sentences written on number cards. The cards could be 5 x 2 = 10, 2 x 5 = 10, 10 ÷ 2 = 5 and 10 ÷ 5 = 2. Then remove one card – 10 ÷ ☐ = 5. Ask the children to identify the card you have removed.

◆ Plenary session

+ Let the groups contribute what they have done. The focus group can show and describe their arrays.
+ Conclude with an enormous addition sum, for example 3 + 3 + 3 + 3 + 3 + 3 and ask the children how you can write it much more quickly.

◆ ◆ ◆ ◆ ◆ ◆ ◆

◆ Starting point: whole class

+ Distinguish between 'everyone must have an equal share' (this aspect of division is called sharing) and 'give out the jewels in 3s and see how many pirates can have 3 – and some might not get any.' (This aspect of division is called repeated equal subtraction.) You could do 'grouping' stories and 'sharing' stories on different days. Set up a 'grouping' story (where you decide on the size of the groups from the beginning.) The pirate king and queen decide to give out a chest of 12 jewels, 3 to each pirate. Draw a picture of the story. 'There were enough for 4 pirates to have 3.'

+ The king and queen decide to share out a chest of 10 jewels. 'This time make it fair shares for everyone' said Pete very loudly. So they shared equally between the 5 pirates.

+ Now or at another lesson have 5 pirates and a chest of 12 so some are left over.

Multiplication and division

◆ Group activities

Focus group

Make an interactive display. Using margarine pots for pirate treasure chests, the children work in pairs with a given number of jewels. They must share out the jewels equally and put lids on the pots so that no-one can see in them, making a number sentence but keeping that secret for now. They should bring their treasure chests to the plenary session together with their number sentences.

"We had 21 jewels and we shared them equally between 3 treasure chests. How many in each of our chests?"

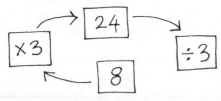

Teacher independent groups

Group 1: Set up some sharing stories on tape, such as 10 buns to share equally between 5 pirates. Let the children record in their own way as this can help you to assess who is understanding.

Group 2: Give the children number cards, cards with division and equals signs and Blu-tack. Ask them to draw and write about some division stories and make a number sentence with the cards to go with

their pictures, such as '16 buns at the baker's shop. How many bags of 4 buns can the baker make?' Write out the questions or put them on tape.

Group 3: Make more complex number stories, maybe some with remainders. The children should draw and write a number sentence to go with each picture. Some of them might be able to use a number line to show repeated subtraction (grouping), such as '24 jewels, how many pirates can have 8 each?'

◆ Plenary session

✦ Everyone should try to work out how many jewels the focus group has in their chests.
✦ Ask group 1 children to talk you through their sharing stories.
✦ Group 2 and 3 show their number sentences with division signs. Give the whole class experience of reading these number sentences, for example '12 buns shared into 3 groups is 4 in a group'.
✦ Demonstrate equal hops back on the number line and link that to taking away the same number each time.

◆ Further activities

✦ Use Generic sheet 4 (page 93) to show the link between multiplication and division.

✦ Play 'grab for gold' in groups of 4. Players take turns to take a big handful of gold (yellow cubes) from a pot and share these out equally between the number of pirates indicated on a spinner (see right). The players keep any gold left over after the sharing out, but return the equal groupings to the pot. The winner is the player with the least gold at the end.

◆ Extension

✦ Play 'lots of' with a dice and a spinner marked to show 'lots of'. Make the arrays with cubes. The winner is the player with the most cubes after 3 goes each.

◆ Support

✦ Ask these children to make up 'lots of'. "Make 3 lots of 4." This will reinforce the language and ensure these children are understanding the basic concept of multiplication.

50
©Hopscotch Educational Publishing

developing
Numeracy
Skills

Numeracy
Year 2/P3

✦ Share the treasure ✦

✦ Start with | 12 | jewels.

✦ Make

2 lots of [ ] makes [ ]

Change it!   Draw the jewels in the chests.

6 lots of [ ] makes | 12 |

Change it!   Draw the jewels in the chests.

3 lots of [ ] makes | 12 |

✦ Find another way with 12. Draw it.

[ ] lots of [ ] makes [ ]

  Now try with 16.

◆ **Share the treasure** ◆

◆ Start with [16] jewels.

◆ Make

2 lots of 8 makes [ ]

Change it! Draw the jewels in the chests.

[ ] lots of 2 makes [ ]

2 + 2 + 2 + 2 + 2 + 2 + 2 + 2 = [ ]   x   [ ]   = 16

Change it! Draw the jewels in the chests.

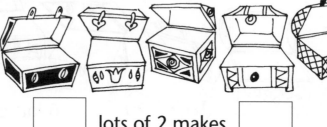

[ ] lots of [ ] = 16

4 + 4 + [ ] + [ ] = 16

[ ] X [ ] = 16

 Now try with 24.

◆ Share the treasure ◆

◆ Start with  jewels.

◆ Draw the jewels in equal groups.

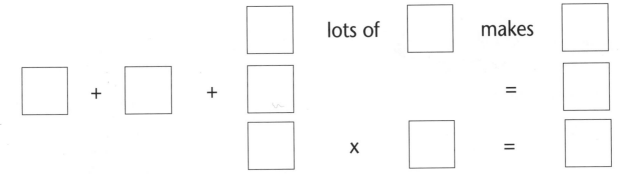

Change it!   Draw the jewels in a different way.

📖 Try with other numbers.

Problems and money

◆ Overall learning objectives

◆ Choose and use appropriate operations for number stories (+, –, x, ÷).
◆ Make estimates and predictions, giving reasons for them.
◆ Solve simple problems with money.
◆ Recognise all coins and exchange pennies for higher values.
◆ Find totals and work out change, and begin to use £. p notation for money.

◆ LESSON ONE TELLING TALES

◆ Assessment focus

Can the children choose and use appropriate operations for number stories?

◆ Resources

◆ number cards
◆ a large quantity of pennies (real and plastic) and other coins
◆ jugs, metre sticks and so on
◆ cubes to represent gold coins and jewels

◆ Oral work and mental calculation

Linking multiplication and division

◆ Play 'Fair shares?' You choose a number card, such as 15, and show it to all the children. This is the number of pennies to share fairly between the pirates. Ask, *"How many could have a fair share?"* The children choose from their number cards a number of pirates that could have an equal share of 15 pennies, so they could choose 15, or 5, or 3. Talk about how many each pirate would have and link this to multiplication. 15 shared equally between 5 pirates is 3 each because 5 x 3 is 15. (See Chapter 8.)

◆ Starting point: whole class

◆ Give experience of stories with addition, subtraction, multiplication and division, asking the children which kind of calculation they did, and writing the calculations on the board. *"Pirate Percy buried 10 chests of treasure but he can only find 6 of them. How many has he lost? How did you work that out? Did you add or subtract?"* (You can use either 10 – 6 = 4 or 6 + something makes 10.)
◆ Give experience with two-stage calculations. *"A pirate had 21 parrots. That was too many so she gave away 18 of them, but 6 of those were given back."*
◆ *"I saw a pirate with 6 jewelled crowns and each crown had 4 jewels in it. How many jewels altogether?"* (This can be repeated addition and multiplication.) Emphasise that this is a 'lots of' story.
◆ *"I saw 10 flocks of parrots, 5 parrots to a flock. How many parrots?"*
◆ You can make quick sketches on the board of the stories just to give children an idea of what they can do for the group work. If the children are confident enough with real money, they could make up money stories.

◆ Group activities

 Focus group

Make up stories as suggested for the groups and use this as time to assess how each individual is coping with the four operations and their ability to check both using the inverse operation and their knowledge of the links between the operations. They can make up stories for you to show at the plenary session, maybe making their drawings large for display.

 Teacher independent groups

Group 1: *"Make up some stories where you have to add and take away. Draw your stories."* You might want to suggest children draw their stories in three stages using three empty story boxes.

Problems and money

Group 2: Ask this group to make up four stories, one that uses addition, one for subtraction, one for 'lots of' and one for sharing equally. Ask them to draw their stories.

Group 3: These children can do the same as group 2, or you could ask just for 'lots of' and sharing stories.

✦ Plenary session

✦ Go through a selection of stories asking what kind of calculation they needed to do. Link addition and subtraction and multiplication and division and demonstrate how to check the calculation with the inverse operation. Where children have done 'lots of' stories, show how they could write those as multiple additions or as multiplications.

✦ This story maths is very important and many children find it hard to know what kind of calculation they need to do so repeat the activity in mental maths time frequently.

✦ LESSON TWO ✦ WOULD YOU RATHER ... ?

✦ Assessment focus

Can the children exchange pennies for higher values?

✦ Resources

✦ a large quantity of pennies (real and plastic) and other coins
✦ *Would you rather..?* by John Burningham a delightful book in which children are given a range of strange choices!
✦ lots of cubes to represent pirate gold coins

✦ Oral work and mental calculation

Simple problems with money

✦ Write up some simple prices on the board, such as coconuts 20p each, bananas 10p, mangoes 50p, and ask the children how much 2/5/10 would cost and so on. For example, if dates cost 10 pence a bunch, how many bunches can I buy for 20p/£1?

"Pirate Pete has £1 to spend on mangoes, how many can he buy?" Have some items at just a few pence and ask the children how much 10 would cost, for example apples are 7 pence each, how much for ten?

✦ Starting point: whole class

✦ Read the story *Would you rather..?* to the children.
✦ Set up a table top shop to give experience with handling money. Use cubes or bottle tops to represent pirate gold coins so that the children can grasp the idea of the lesson even if they lack experience with real coins.
✦ Set up some problems then ask small groups to find out the answers. Ask them to make estimates and predictions first, although some of them will find that hard if they have not had much experience of using money.
  • Would you rather have a litre jug full of gold coins, or two metres of coins?
  • Would you rather have a yoghurt pot full of pennies or a tower 20 cm tall of pennies?
  • Would you rather have a handful of pennies or a pound coin?
  • Would you rather have a metre of pennies or 4 fifty pence pieces?

Problems and money

✦ You could ask the children to bring a few pennies to school to collect money for a charity. *"How much money do you think we would collect if we collected enough pennies to go right across our room/ fill the yellow pencil pot?"*

✦ Group activities

Focus group

With children who still need a great deal of help with money, do some counting of pennies, maybe a yoghurt pot full, then exchange them for coins of higher value. Ask them to pick up coins with the same value as 10 pennies, 2 ten pence pieces, 5 twenty pence pieces and so on.

Teacher independent groups

Use the photocopiable activity sheets.

Activity sheet 1: You need a large pot of pennies, cubes, buttons or counters to represent gold coins for this activity. If you have children who still need to work with numbers under 20, use pennies/cubes for

both questions. You might need to sit a confident child with this group while they take their handful of pennies/cubes and then count them putting them into groups of 10. If you have time, you can help the children to exchange those pennies for other coins to work out how much money they have.

Activity sheet 2: Help these children to make estimates first of the bills. Pete's shopping bill comes to £1.50 and Pam's is £1.25.

Activity sheet 3: Percy's shopping bill is £3.10 and Pat's is £3.20.

✦ Plenary session

✦ Each group can say what they found out. Talk about making rough estimates first. These estimates will often not be exactly right but that doesn't matter. Making a guess first can help children to see if they have a reasonable answer. *"If you added up Pete's bill and got £100 you would know you were wrong somewhere."*

✦ Further activities

✦ Make up more problems, such as 'Would you rather have one share of 9 buns between 3 people or 4 buns between 4 people?'

✦ Extension

✦ Would you rather have your height in a tower of pennies or a metre of ten pences laid edge to edge? (Pennies made into a tower are about 6 pennies to each cm, so 1 metre would be about 600 pence. There are about 5 ten pence pieces to every 12 cm, so a metre is about 40 tens, making £4.) Challenge the children to work it out making smaller measurements then calculating.

✦ Support

✦ Make sure the children can recognise all coins. Ask parents to let their children identify coins in their purse and start to add up small amounts of money.

✦ Play a simple money game just with pennies using generic sheet 6 (page 95). No reading is involved if you put amounts to pay to the bank in a circle, for example ⓵p, and amounts not in a circle mean they win that much. The children each start with 20 pennies and they both go the same way round the track, throwing a dice to show how many spaces to move. The winner is the player who gets back to the ship with the most money.

56
©Hopscotch Educational Publishing

developing
Numeracy
Skills

Numeracy
Year 2/P3

✦ Would you rather...? ✦

✦ Would you rather have a handful of
  pennies or 100 pennies?

 = ☐   I'd rather have _____

✦ Would you rather have one litre of gold
  coins or a metre of gold coins?

1 litre = ☐ gold coins   1 metre = ☐ gold coins

I'd rather have _____

   Make up a 'Would you rather...?' for a friend.

✦ **Would you rather…?** ✦

coconuts
20p

bananas
5p

mangoes
10p

dates
25p bunch

✦ Would you rather pay Pete's or Pam's
   shopping bill?

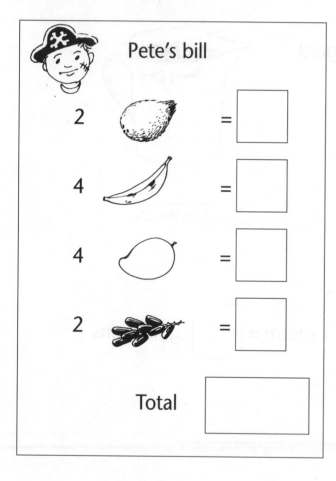

Pete's bill

2 ⬭ = ☐

4 🍌 = ☐

4 ⬭ = ☐

2 🫐 = ☐

Total ☐

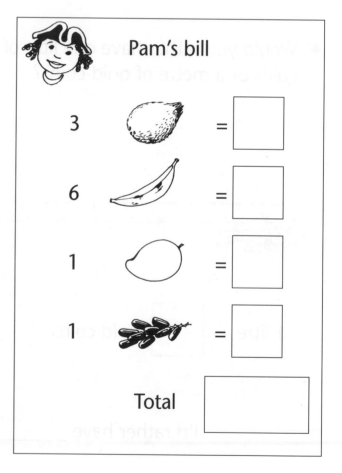

Pam's bill

3 ⬭ = ☐

6 🍌 = ☐

1 ⬭ = ☐

1 🫐 = ☐

Total ☐

I would rather _____

 Buy fruit for exactly £1.

developing
Numeracy
Skills

Photocopiable

✦ Would you rather...? ✦

coconuts
20p

bananas
5p

mangoes
10p

dates
25p bunch

✦ Would you rather pay Percy's or Pat's shopping bill?

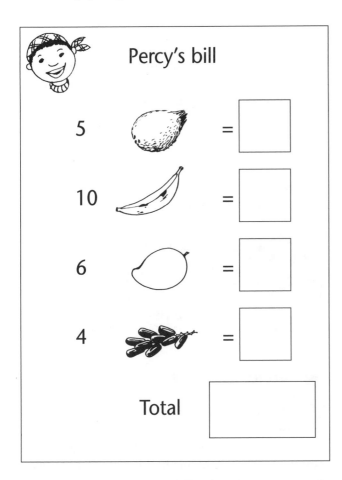

Percy's bill

5 🥥 = ☐

10 🍌 = ☐

6 🥭 = ☐

4 🫐 = ☐

Total ☐

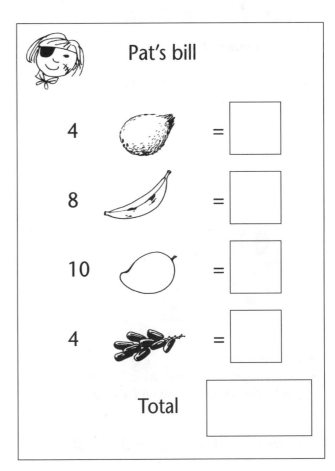

Pat's bill

4 🥥 = ☐

8 🍌 = ☐

10 🥭 = ☐

4 🫐 = ☐

Total ☐

I would rather _____

_____

 Buy fruit for exactly £5.

developing
Numeracy
Skills

Number stories and fractions

✦ Overall learning objectives

+ Recognise and find one half and one quarter of shapes and small numbers.
+ Begin to recognise equivalence of fractions, halves and quarters.
+ Explain how a problem was solved.
+ Recognise simple equivalent fractions.

✦ LESSON ONE PIRATE PARTY

✦ Assessment focus

Can the children explain how a problem was solved?

✦ Resources

+ fraction cards showing halves and quarters

+ plain biscuits
+ round paper pizzas and cakes, rectangles for sandwiches, flags and so on for a party

✦ Oral work and mental calculation

Wholes, halves and quarters

+ Gradually build up a set of fraction cards that children can understand. Hold them up and ask the children to say which fraction each card shows. They will need to be familiar with these and the fractions they show in order to do Lesson Two.

✦ Starting point: whole class

+ Do a whole-class real problem with plain biscuits. The children should wash their hands and get into groups of 2, 3, 4 or 5. Give each group an awkward number of biscuits for their size of group, such as 11 or 13 for the group of 5, and 7 for the group of 2. No-one is to eat anything yet! They need to share out the biscuits fairly, breaking them when they need to, then draw what they did and explain how much each person had. (Expect them to name some fractions as 'a little bit' – that is fine at this stage.) They then draw what they found out – then eat their share of biscuits.

+ Then set up a story situation of pirates having a party. They want to have pizzas, sandwiches, cakes and fair shares of biscuits, and drink. Using paper circles for pizzas and cakes, squares for sandwiches and so on, show the children how to fold or cut one in half to share between two pirates. Make it clear that halves are always equal – although that was too hard to do with the biscuits. Tell them there is no such thing as a bigger half. Show how to fold a paper pizza in half then half again to make quarters.

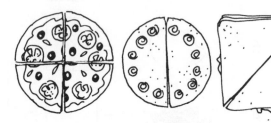

✦ Group activities

 Focus group

Do some paper folding to show how two halves is equal to a whole and one half is equivalent to two quarters. As well as using pizzas, you can prepare some rectangles (planks) to help with Lesson Two.

1 whole			
half		$\frac{1}{2}$	
$\frac{1}{4}$	$\frac{1}{4}$	$\frac{1}{4}$	$\frac{1}{4}$

Number stories and fractions

Teacher independent groups

Group 1: These children need two whole pizzas, one cake, and four play people (pirates). Ask them to fold or cut the pizza in halves and the cake into quarters. They should share the food among the four pirates and draw and stick what they did.

Group 2: These children need three pizzas. They should cut these into quarters and share them between four pirates – three quarters each. They can have sandwiches and cakes to share as well. They should draw and stick what they have done for the plenary session and write a sentence about their work.

Group 3: These children could try five pirates with three pizzas and four cakes and try to make equal shares. They will find they are left with a half pizza to share between five. Let them talk about the very small piece left over, smaller than a quarter. The cake will give each pirate three quarters and again a bit is left over.

✦ *Plenary session*

✦ Let the children talk about what they did, including their problems and the decisions they made to solve them.

✦ Talk about real problems at home with cutting things to share them.

✦ *"So you can see how useful maths is to us in our life. We use it all the time."*

✦ LESSON TWO ✦ WALK THE PLANK

✦ *Assessment focus*

Can the children recognise simple equivalent fractions?

✦ *Resources*

✦ a kitchen timer or alarm clock
✦ paper circles
✦ fraction cards (as in Lesson One)
✦ a paper 'plank' marked as below

$\frac{1}{2}$	$\frac{1}{4}$	$\frac{1}{4}$

✦ *Oral work and mental calculation*

Telling the time and the passage of time

✦ Set a kitchen timer or alarm clock to ring in ten minutes and spend the time working on time problems such as reading 'half past' and 'quarter

past' times on a large teaching clock. Link half and quarter folded paper circles to the times on a clock.

✦ *Starting point: whole class*

✦ To play 'walk the plank' you need your collection of fraction cards. Put the children into small groups. Each group needs one paper 'plank' – a length of newspaper will do. They first fold and mark their plank into four quarters. Establish that there are 2 halves and 4 quarters. Then a child from each group takes a fraction card from the box (without looking) and this card tells that group how far along the plank they are to walk. If they pick a 'whole one' first time they have to walk their plank and they are in the sea. If they get a card with less than that, they put it down on their plank, so if their card shows a half, they put

Number stories and fractions

their card (or a model pirate) half way along their plank. Go round the groups a second time for any who aren't in the sea. They take another card and add the amount to the card they already have on their plank.

✦ By the end of two rounds, some children will still not have a whole one and they are the winners.

◆ Group activities

Focus group

Do paper folding, or play the 'walk the plank' game with this small group, observing who is able to talk about equivalent fractions.

Teacher independent groups

Use the photocopiable activity sheets.

Activity sheet 1: Encourage the children to think of a different way to colour their flag from those around them. Establish that the lower flag will only be half coloured in. They can use plastic shapes and rulers, or fold paper to make their own flags.

Activity sheet 2: These are more complex flags and they will have a quarter not coloured in the second row. Their own design will be completely coloured. The symbol for $\frac{1}{4}$ has been used on all the sheets.

Activity sheet 3: These are complex designs. Challenge these children to come up with a half that no-one else has found. It may help if they try it out on scrap paper first.

◆ Plenary session

✦ Point out that halves must be the same size, and all the quarters need to be the same size. Ask about some equivalent fractions. *"What is the same size as a half?"* (Two quarters.) *"How many quarters make a whole one?"* *"So your flag has the same amount of blue, yellow, red and green does it?"* *"How many quarters make a half?"*
✦ *"What did you enjoy in maths today?"*
✦ *"What was hard in maths today?"*

◆ Further activities

✦ Give experience of finding halves and quarters of numbers, such as sharing eight dates between four pirates fairly or 'give a quarter of these dates to each pirate'. Explain that when they come to choosing their own numbers for sharing dates, they need to think very carefully about their 4 times table.
✦ See also making flags in chapter 13.

◆ Extension

✦ *"Can you find 10 different ways to colour half of the top two flags on Activity sheet 3 which have 16 small squares?"* (There are hundreds of different ways. Opposite is just one example.)

◆ Support

✦ Find halves of small numbers and relate this to the 2 times table. Make number cards with the answer of half the number on the back for a teacher independent activity. As children learn them, add more cards.

Activity 1

✦ Colour the flags ✦

✦ Colour half of each flag in blue.

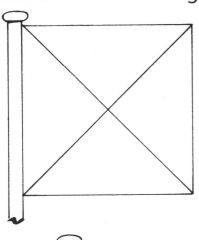

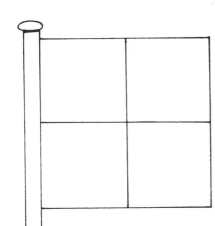

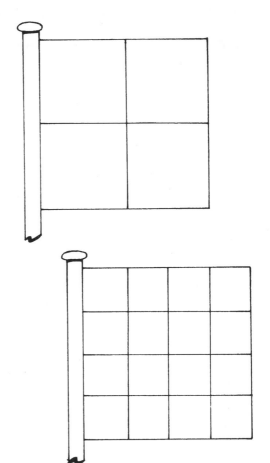

✦ Colour   blue and   yellow.

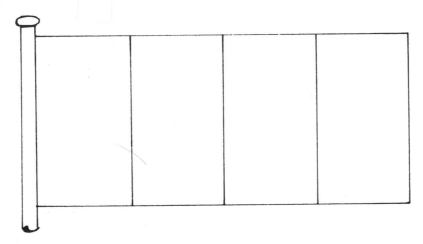

 Make more flags.

✦ Colour the flags ✦

✦ Colour half of each flag in red.

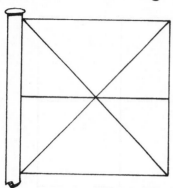
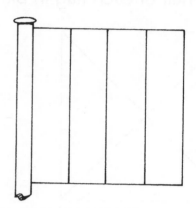

✦ Colour half of each flag in red ... yellow.

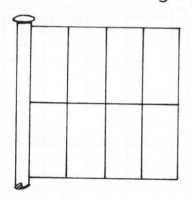
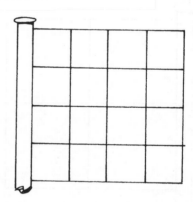

✦ Make your own flag. Colour half of it in red ... yellow
and ½ green.

 Make more flags.

Photocopiable

©Hopscotch Educational Publishing

✦ Colour the flags ✦

✦ Colour half of each flag in green.

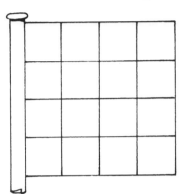
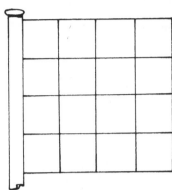

✦ Colour half of each flag in green and $\frac{1}{4}$ yellow.

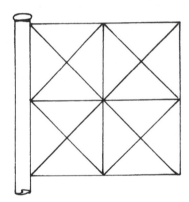
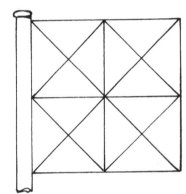

✦ Design your own flag. Colour each $\frac{1}{4}$ in a different colour.

 Make more flags.

Measuring

 Overall learning objectives

- Use a metre stick appropriately.
- Measure length and capacity.
- Make direct comparisons and use the language of comparison.
- Measure using litres and millilitres.
- Read a scale to the nearest labelled division.

 **LESSON ONE
HOW MANY?**

 Assessment focus

Can the children use a ruler and metre stick appropriately?

 Resources

- metre sticks, rulers, tape measures and cubes
- newspaper, scissors, sticky tape
- cubes

 Oral work and mental calculation

Doubling and doubling again

- Go over all the doubles to 20 or 30 or to suit your children. Try some simple numbers showing how to double again. For example, start with 2, double it to get 4, then double that number to get 8. Write up the numbers on the board and ask the children to explain what is happening to the number you first started with. (You end up with 4 lots of that starting number, so this is one way to do the 4 times table if you know your 2x table.)

Starting point: whole class

- Tell the children about the 'walking the plank' game (see Chapter 10, Lesson Two) and tell them that they are going to make a plank that is about four children's paces. They are going to do that by

measuring one pace, then doubling that length, then doubling the new length. (An easy version of this lesson is for children just to measure one pace of four children in a group and stick them together.) Demonstrate a pace – one ordinary step, not a big stride. Talk about where to measure from – let the children make some decision about this – maybe everyone needs to do it from the back of one foot to the front of the other.

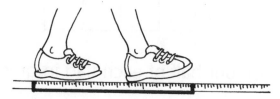

- Demonstrate with one child, showing how to use a metre rule (point out the 'dead space' at the start of the ruler), starting at 0 and reading the centimetres. Put the children in groups of 4. It can help you to see how well they have measured if they draw around each foot on the newspaper.

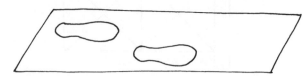

 Group activities

Focus group

Try to get round to watching as many children as possible using a metre rule. Question them about where they start to measure and so on. You could have some strips of paper or lines of cubes for them to measure as you observe them. Write each child's pace measurement in centimetres on the board (and on their newspaper pace), as you will need these for Lesson Two.

Tomas 54 cms

Eli 57 cms

Catrin 61 cms

Measuring

 Teacher independent groups

Group 1: This group can make a line of cubes as long as 1 (or 4) of their paces. Let them compare this with a metre rule. *"My plank is longer than a metre." "Mine is about a metre and a half."* Help them to read the centimetre measurement.

Group 2: These children should cut out a pace each, write on it the length in centimetres, then find a way to work out how long 4 paces will be. *"Is it as long as 2 metre sticks?"*

Group 3: This group can double their centimetre measure then double that measurement and cut out a paper plank.

LESSON TWO
THIRSTY WORK

◆ Assessment focus

Can the children read a scale to the nearest labelled division?

◆ Resources

+ litre jugs and lots of mugs all the same size
+ a variety of plastic bottles and pots
+ lots of newspaper/cloths
+ paper scale or pretend thermometer

◆ Oral work and mental calculation

Reading a scale

+ Lay out a paper 'scale', or a pretend thermometer, on the floor and point out how like a number line it is. Show the children how this is a large version of what is up the side of a measuring jug and other measuring items. Explain that it is important they learn to read a scale. Position a

◆ Plenary session

+ Hold up some of the paces or planks and compare them. Talk about the measurement in metres ('about one and a half metres') and ask the children in group 1 to compare paces or planks using words 'longer/longest' and so on. Read the pace measurements with all the children. *"Ben's pace is 51 cm. Jon's is 54. About how long will 4 of their paces be, longer than a metre or about 2 metres?"*
+ Ask for rules for how you use a metre stick properly. *"Where do you start to measure from?"* and so on.
+ *"Is it true that if you double a measurement, then double that new measurement, you end up with 4 times the first measurement?"*

red arrow (or a yoghurt pot) on the scale and ask the children to 'read' it, saying 'almost' 2 litres and so on. (Later in the year you can move on to rounding up and down where necessary.)

"Let's pretend this is a measuring jug scale. It reads almost 2 litres."

◆ Starting point: whole class

+ Tell the children *"The pirates are going to get very hot today because they are going to dig holes to bury lots of treasure chests. They want to make sure that they take enough drink with them for four mugs of drink each. You are the pirates – you will work in groups of four."* Hold up some plastic bottles and ask if the children think they will hold 4 lots of 4 mugs of water. Demonstrate measuring water in a litre jug and show them how to read the scale.
+ Organise the children into groups and give out mugs and bottles to each group. (Put down newspaper.)

Measuring

◆ Group activities

Focus group

Work with the children to make a bottle that measures in mugs-full. Stick a bit of paper on the side of a tall narrow bottle. The children pour in a mug at a time and mark where it comes to on the paper strip. Help children individually to read a scale on a litre jug.

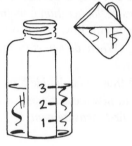

Teacher independent groups

Use the photocopiable activity sheets.

Activity sheet 1: These children have to work out how many of their bottles they will need for 16 mugs full of drink for the pirates. They should draw the bottles they need for the 16 mugs-full, then read a simple scale of mugs-full. (About 7 mugs-full.) They should then copy their pace measurement from Lesson One, then make a paper hat.

Activity sheet 2: If equipment is in limited supplies, this group could do the second and last parts of this sheet first. Their measuring jug to read is in millilitres in multiples of 100 and the amount is about 600 ml.

Activity sheet 3: These children should measure the amount of drink using a litre jug. Encourage them to round measurements up or down – *"We need about a litre and a half"*. The measuring jugs are about 700 ml and about a litre and a half (1 litre 500 ml.)

◆ Plenary session

◆ Make the point that we try to measure very carefully, but almost always in real life we make approximate measurements as well, so we say we need 'about' 2 litres and so on.
◆ Repeat the activity reading a scale/thermometer/ruler drawn on the board.

◆ Further activities

◆ Each thirsty pirate wants 1 litre to drink. How much drink for 10 thirsty pirates?
◆ The children could compare the length of a plank with their height.
◆ Make an 'instant graph' by putting up the planks next to each other in order of length.
◆ If you are able to make up squash so that everyone can have a mug-full that makes the problems more real. *"About how many litres will we need?"*
◆ Help the children to read a thermometer and take temperature measurements for a whole week to help with this.
◆ On the theme of pirates, the children could weigh playdough 'jewels' or fill Polydron treasure chests (see Chapter 13) with pebbles

for jewels. *"Who had a treasure chest that weighed less than one kilogram?"*

◆ Extension

◆ Measure your height then double it and double it again.

◆ Support

◆ Work with this group to measure round their heads to make a pirate hat. Go over the use of a ruler again.
◆ Children can use the jug marked in mugs-full for more capacity work. Supervise some reading from that scale to check who has understood.

✦ Can you measure? ✦

 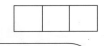

4 pirates

4 mugs each

Draw the bottles they need.

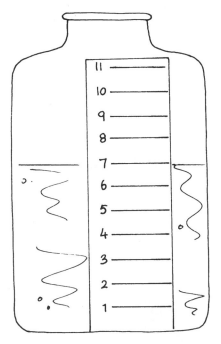

This bottle holds about ☐ mugs-full

There are about ☐ mugs-full of water in it.

My pace is ☐ cm long.

 Measure round your head.

Round my head is _____ cms.

Make a paper hat.

✦ Can you measure? ✦

 4 pirates

4 mugs each

Draw the bottles they need.

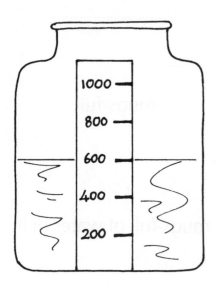

This bottle holds about _____ ml.

It has about _____ ml of water in it.

My pace is [ ] cm long.

4 paces is [ ] cm long.

 Round my head is _____ cms.

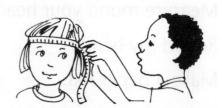

✦ Can you measure? ✦

 4 pirates

 4 mugs each

They need _____ litres of drink

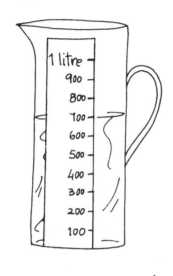

_____ ml   _____ litres

My pace is [   ] cm long.

4 paces is [   ] cm long.

 Round my head is _____ cms.

Handling data

✦ *Overall learning objectives*

- ✦ Sort numbers and shapes into appropriate tables and sets and talk about their work.
- ✦ Solve a problem by gathering relevant information and sorting it.
- ✦ Make a block graph and pictogram.
- ✦ Properties and vocabulary of shape.

◆ LESSON ONE
SORTING JEWELS

✦ *Assessment focus*

Can the children sort numbers and shapes into appropriate sets and talk about their work?

✦ *Resources*

- ✦ number cards
- ✦ plastic 2D shapes and irregular 2D shapes made from coloured paper for jewels (include some with right angles)
- ✦ small margarine tubs/bags for jewel bags

✦ *Oral work and mental calculation*

Sorting numbers

- ✦ Use ropes to make two sets on the carpet. Name the two groups, for example 'even numbers' and 'numbers that are multiples of 5'.

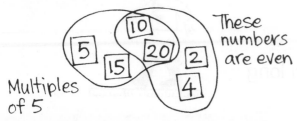

- ✦ Sort number cards into the appropriate set and make lists on the board. *"What will we do about numbers that end in zero? They are multiples of 5 and they are even as well."* Ask what the children would do with numbers such as 7. (This cannot be

included in either group so it goes outside both of the groups in the universal set of numbers.)

	even	not even
multiples of 5	10 20	5 15
not multiples of 5	14	7 3

✦ *Starting point: whole class*

- ✦ *"The pirate king and queen want to sort out their jewels into 4 treasure chests."* Lay out a grid on the carpet like this.

	3 sides	not 3 sides
regular	△ △	☐ ⬡
not regular	◺	◹ ⬠

(It is important that we give children experience with shapes that are not regular.)
- ✦ Together the children sort the jewels (shapes), into the 4 treasure chests.
- ✦ Find other ways to sort, for example those with straight sides, those with curved sides, those with right angles (square corners) and those without right angles. (Group 3 will need to be clear about square corners for their activity.)

✦ *Group activities*

    Focus group

- ✦ Set out a variety of shapes and trays with labels on them, for example 'shapes with 5 corners and 5 sides', 'shapes with 4 square corners but sides not equal', 'shapes with 4 straight equal sides' and 'other shapes with 4 sides'. The children sort the plastic and paper shapes into the groups. Assess their language of shape as well as their ability to give reasons for decisions they have made in sorting.

Handling data

 Teacher independent groups

Use the photocopiable activity sheets

Note: Groups 2 and 3 will need a jewel bag (one for about every 3 or 4 children) to use with the sheets.

Activity sheet 1: The children sort the jewels into the appropriate treasure chest. For the next part they will need a tray of shapes. Encourage them not to draw around the shapes but to copy them (some children might need help to do that).

Activity sheet 2: These children sort the jewels, then using a bag of 'jewels' they sort in any way they choose. The jewel bags need to have a good variety in them but, for this group, only about 8 or 10 jewels. They don't need to use every jewel when they sort them and there is no limit to the number of groups they can make.

Activity sheet 3: Remind this group what a square corner is, identifying the right angle in shapes for the first treasure chest. They could use a set square or a plastic rectangle to help to draw their right angles and they might also want a ruler and stencils. Their jewel bag could be more complex, maybe with 12 to 15 jewels.

◆ *Plenary session*

◆ Look at children's drawn treasure chests on the sheets, talking about why shapes are in particular sets. Identify square corners for everyone.

◆ Look at how the children have sorted their jewel bags, asking them to justify their decisions. Point out that in maths there is often more than one way to do something and often there isn't a 'right' answer.

◆ *"What did you enjoy most in maths today?"*

LESSON TWO COLLECTING DATA

◆ *Assessment focus*

Can the children solve a problem by gathering relevant information and sorting it in a simple way?

◆ *Resources*
◆ number cards
◆ a metal plate for spinning
◆ squares of paper for the pictograms

◆ *Oral work and mental calculation*

Finding differences

◆ Give every child a number card face down. One child goes to the front and says the names of two children, then spins a metal plate on the floor, (or you can spin the plate). The two children hold up their number cards (they might need to call out

the number as well) and before the plate stops spinning, the whole group must call out the difference between the two numbers, (or hold up number cards). For a slower game, two children stand out the front and select a card each face down and the group calculates without a spinning plate.

◆ *Starting point: whole class*

◆ Suggest a hypothesis that you can test out, such as 'the favourite pirate story in our class is *The Man Whose Mother Was a Pirate*'. List about 3 or 4 pirate stories on the board. Each child makes a smiley face on a square of paper and writes their name on it. They stick their face next to their favourite story with Blu-tack. Make it clear that the faces must be lined up on the pictogram.

The man whose mother...	☺	☺	☺	☺	☺
Captain Pugwash	☺	☺	☺	☺	
Jolly Roger	☺	☺	☺		
Treasure of Cosy Cove	☺				

Handling data

- The four suggested books are: *The Man Whose Mother Was a Pirate* by Margaret Mahy, *Captain Pugwash* by John Ryan, *Jolly Roger* by Colin McNaughton and *Treasure of Cosy Cove* by Tony Ross.
- Discuss questions that arise from the pictogram, such as 'How many more children like Captain Pugwash than like Jolly Roger?'
- To prepare children for the group work, let them suggest problems they want to find answers to. Refine these before they set about collecting data. Phrase the problems as a hypothesis – a suggestion of something that we can answer by collecting data, for example 'Most children in our class like peanut butter better than chocolate spread'. Do some preliminary shows of hands to help to word the hypothesis.

◆ Group activities

Focus group

Ideally use a computer to enter some data to produce some graphs that you can talk about at review time. Numerical data is best, for example the number of brothers and sisters in a family. Or use the pictogram made in the starter as a basis for answering questions.

 Teacher independent groups

Group 1: These children can gather data just from their group and make a list and then a block graph with cubes, such as on 'The favourite colours in our group.'

Group 2: This group collects data to answer a hypothesis, such as 'Children in our class like *Neighbours* better than *Blue Peter*'. They can make a pictogram.

Group 3: This group can do the same as group 2. They can then write three questions to ask the others at group time about their pictogram.

◆ Plenary session

- Use the questions that the group 3 children have made then formulate more questions that arise from the children's pictograms, such as 'How many more children like blue than green?' and 'What is the difference between the number of children who like *Neighbours* best, and the number who like *Blue Peter* best?'
- *"Is there something else you would like to find out about? What could you do to find out?"*

◆ Further activities

- Play a game with cards 0–9 working in pairs. The children shuffle the cards and choose 6 then make 6 two-digit numbers. For example, with 2 and 4 you could make 24 and 42. They should find a way to sort their 6 numbers and make a quick sketch of the sets, including any numbers they couldn't include.

◆ Extension

- Ask the children to think of something that would be really interesting to find out about. Perhaps they could ask children in other classes at playtime.

◆ Support

- Make other quick pictograms just with a small group using very simple data, such as what they ate for breakfast or the month of their birthday.

◆ Sort the jewels ◆

◆ Sort these jewels into the treasure chests.

jewels with
3 sides

jewels with
4 sides

◆ Draw jewels for this chest.

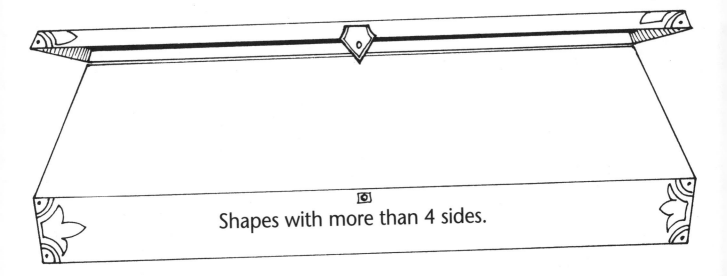

Shapes with more than 4 sides.

📖 Find some jewels with curved sides.
Draw them.

✦ Sort the jewels ✦

✦ Sort these jewels into the treasure chests.

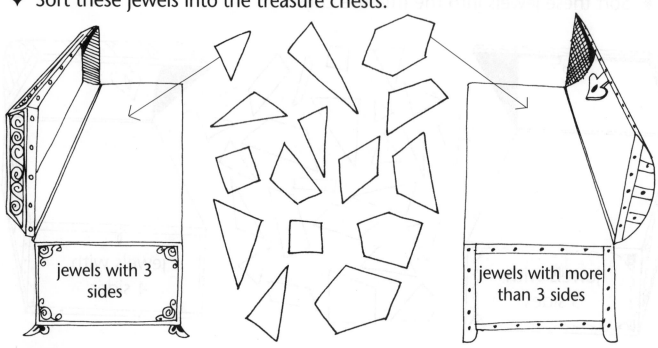

✦ Find a way to sort your jewel bag.
Draw what you did.

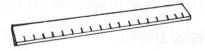 Use a ruler. Draw a set of jewels that
have 4 unequal sides.

developing
Numeracy Skills

Name _____

✦ Sort the jewels ✦

✦ Draw some jewels in these treasure chests.

 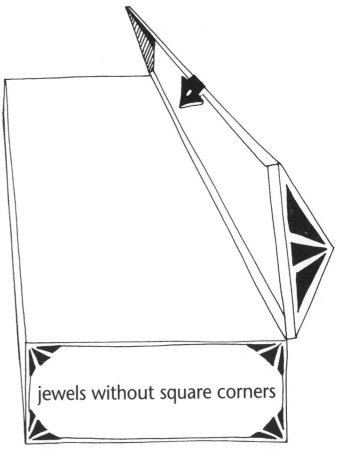

jewels with square corners

jewels without square corners

✦ Find a way to sort your jewel bag. Draw what you did.

 Draw jewels with 4 sides. Try to make them all different.

Problems and shape

Overall learning objectives

✦ Recognise a line of symmetry.
✦ Name and describe 3D shapes.
✦ Relate 3D shapes to pictures of them.

LESSON ONE
LINE SYMMETRY

Assessment focus

Can the children recognise a line of symmetry?

Resources

✦ number cards
✦ interlocking cubes
✦ some symmetrical and non-symmetrical pictures
  (see the activity sheets)
✦ lots of rectangles of scrap paper
✦ mirrors

Oral work and mental calculation

Counting up to and beyond 100

✦ Let a child select two number cards from a face
  down pack and make a 2-digit number. For
  example, if 5 and 2 are selected, they can make
  25 or 52. Decide which is the lower number, start
  from that number and count to the larger number
  (and back again if you want). Sometimes they
  could make a number then just count from that
  number up to and beyond 100. To extend the
  game choose three cards and make a three-digit
  number and count from that number up to the
  next 100.

Starting point: whole class

✦ Show the children how to fold and cut or tear
  rectangles of paper. Some might be able to make
  concertina folds and cut.

✦ You could make a book 'Our book of symmetrical
  shapes' or make flags. (See also Chapter 10.)
✦ Some children could come to the front and see
  what happens with mirrors on simple shapes you
  have drawn on the board. Demonstrate how they
  can find a place to put their mirror on a
  symmetrical smiley face and get the same picture
  by looking in the mirror along the line of
  symmetry, whereas if they look at a drawing of a
  ship, it doesn't have a line of symmetry.

✦ Demonstrate symmetrical designs with
  interlocking cubes. Put the children in pairs
  giving each pair a few cubes. They must make a
  simple shape, then give it to another pair who
  make the other symmetrical half. Make sure all
  the children are aware of the line of symmetry
  before you go into group work.

Group activities

   Focus group

Stick some half pictures on paper and ask the
children to draw in the missing half symmetrically.

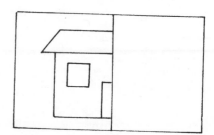

You can use the activity sheets from Lesson Two to
let the children explore patterns with mirrors.

Problems and shape

 Teacher independent groups

Group 1: This group could make some blot pictures or use pegboards or cubes to make symmetrical designs.

Group 2: These children should design a symmetrical flag, or use patterns blocks to make a symmetrical pattern on a board so it can be taken to the plenary session.

Group 3: These children should fold paper by making concertina folds and make a string of people. You need to stress that the people must be holding hands or have feet touching or they will not stay together.

 Plenary session

✦ Look for lines of symmetry in the work the children have done. Ask them to show you where the line is on their work. Inevitably some work will not be symmetrical. *"This isn't quite symmetrical. It would need to have …"* Point out what has made it non-symmetrical. You can make an interactive display with cubes, peg boards and so on for the children to try out their ideas again.

✦ This task works well as a homework challenge. *"Make another design for our class book about symmetry."*

LESSON TWO
GOLD BARS

 Assessment focus

Can the children relate 3D shapes to pictures of them?

 Resources

✦ a variety of boxes, Toblerone, cuboids etc
✦ Polydrons /other construction kits
✦ 3D shapes
✦ cubes
✦ number cards

 Oral work and mental calculation

Ordering numbers to 100

✦ Play 'square race'. Put out number cards 1–100 round the room randomly then delegate small groups to find a group of numbers, such as 1–5, then another group 6–10 and so on. They go and find their numbers then sit down in the circle. Then organise them to put out their cards in lines

starting from 1, so that you build up a 100 square. If you have two sets of cards this makes a good race for two teams, but do it where noise won't matter!

 Starting point: whole class

✦ Choose some boxes of various shapes and also ask a few children to make some simple Polydron shapes, such as a pyramid. Children often make tetrahedrons with Polydrons so you could include that in the shapes. A tetrahedron has 4 triangular faces. Draw the 3D shapes on the board.

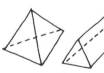

A cuboid, square based pyramid, triangular pyramid and triangular prism.

✦ Show the boxes and models and ask the children to match a shape to each drawing. Give each shape a name where you can and ask the children to describe it. *"This one has a triangular face."* and *"This one has six flat faces."*

Problems and shape

 Put some shapes in a feely bag and pass it round the circle. The children must say what they are feeling and others could try to name the shape.

Group activities

Focus group

Extend the starter activity by introducing more pictures of shapes, such as a cylinder, cone, sphere, cuboid. They must find or make these shapes, give each one a label, then sort the shapes in a variety of ways on a board to show at review time. Assess who was able to match shapes to pictures and who can use the language of shape well – faces and so on.

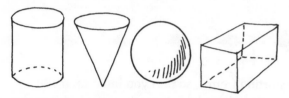

Teacher independent groups

Use the photocopiable activity sheets

Activity sheet 1: The children should make a copy of the gold bars using interlocking cubes and keep these to show at the plenary session. They then use a construction kit to make a treasure chest to hold their gold bars. They can use a mirror to explore the pictures on the treasure chest.

Activity sheet 2: These children should make different gold bars, each made up of 4 cubes. Ask them to see how many different ones they can make. Ask them to flip over some of their shapes and decide if this makes them different. Again they should use a construction kit to make a treasure chest and use mirrors to explore the shapes.

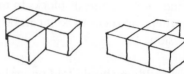

"So are these different?" They might decide they are.

Activity sheet 3: The gold bars for this group are all T-shaped and get larger each time. The children should work co-operatively to make more. Have ready some cuboid boxes for their treasure chests. Again there are pictures to explore with a mirror.

Plenary session

 Let the children show you their gold bars and match their models to the pictures. Group 3 should explain how their gold Ts get bigger. *"Tell me how you knew that was the next one? How did it grow each time?"*

 Look at the boxes/treasure chests. With a cereal box, show how to break a box open to show its net. Relate this to Polydrons and making a net of a cube or cuboid.

Further activities

 The children can make a list of letters of the alphabet that are symmetrical.

 Make a shape game with generic sheet 6 (page 95) drawing 2D shapes in some of the spaces. Play in pairs, throwing the dice in turn and moving that many spaces. If they land on a space with a 2D shape, they pick up a plastic 2D shape and their partner must check that they pick up the right one. If they choose a wrong one they have to put it back. The winner is the player with the most different shapes. Repeats are not counted.

Extension

 Challenge the children to make a cube or cuboid with card and sticky tape.

Support

 Make an interactive display of 3D shapes and their labels. If each label has a length of wool with Blu-tack at the end, they can attach a label to each shape for you to check.

 Give plenty of time with construction kits.

✦ Gold bars ✦

✦ Use cubes to make these gold bars.

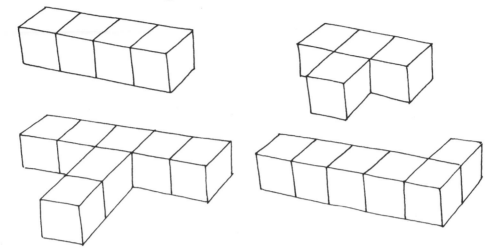

✦ Look at this treasure chest. Draw another symmetrical shape on it.

✦ Make a treasure chest big enough to hold your gold bars.

developing
Numeracy
Skills

Photocopiable

✦ Gold bars ✦

✦ Make these gold bars using 4 cubes.

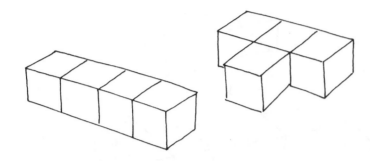

Try to make 2 more.

✦ Look at this treasure chest. Draw another symmetrical shape on it.

✦ Make a treasure chest big enough for all your gold bars.

To make my treasure chest

I used _____

The shape is _____

Name _____

✦ Gold bars ✦

✦ Work with others. Make golden Ts.

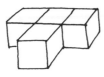 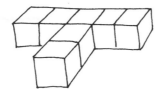 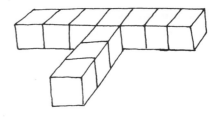

✦ Make the next one in the pattern, and the next.

Count how many cubes in each picture.

How many for the next one?

✦ Look at this treasure chest. Draw another symmetrical shape on it.

✦ Make a treasure chest for your golden Ts.

Photocopiable
©Hopscotch Educational Publishing

Position, direction & movement

 ## Overall learning objectives

✦ Identifying right angles.
✦ Giving instructions for someone else to follow a route.

LESSON ONE
SQUARE CORNERS

 ## Assessment focus

Can the children identify right angles?

 ## Resources

✦ scrap paper
✦ geo-strips, Meccano and so on
✦ 2D shapes
✦ clock stamp and teaching clocks

 ## Oral work and mental calculation

Quarter turns

✦ Ask all the children to stand up and face the same way, then make a small jump round, just a quarter turn. At first hold up your arm and show them which way to turn, then extend the game to saying clockwise/anti-clockwise. Before they jump ask them where they will be facing when they have made the jump. This helps with orientation problems. Extend this in PE to jumping more than one quarter turn. Be explicit that if you turn all the way round (take care, this can be dangerous to jump) you will be turning through 4 quarter turns.

 ## Starting point: whole class

✦ Each child needs a piece of scrap paper of any shape. They fold it into two. (Remind them that these are not halves unless they are very careful). Then they fold that shape into two again putting the two folded edges together carefully. They then

identify the square corner they have made and colour it.

It can be useful to think of the point of the square corner as a nose so you can explain that they put the nose on square corners. A face drawn on the corner can help.

✦ You can demonstrate how they can fit their square corner into other square corners, for example put the nose into the corner of the window, fit it on the edge of a book or the board. Let the children explore this. Then demonstrate what we mean by 'angle' – a movement such as with scissors, two pieces of Meccano, the hands of a clock or a door opening and closing. Ask the children to put their arms at right angles, making a square corner, then change them so that the angle is smaller than a right angle. Explain that a square corner/right angle is a very important angle that we use a great deal.

  ## Group activities

Focus group

Use Meccano or geo-strips to make angles. *"Make your angle larger than a square corner. Now make it smaller."* Use the paper corners from the starter activity to show how two square corners 'nose inwards' make a straight line.

Position, direction & movement

If there is time, the children can make shapes (such as squares) using geo-strips or Meccano, so that the corner angles can be changed from squares to diamond shapes. These could be demonstrated in the plenary session.

 Teacher independent groups

Group 1: These children should make a list of (or draw) some of the square corners they can find in the classroom.

Group 2: This group should draw the times on a clock where the hands make a right angle. (This activity is only suitable for children who can read analogue time.) Others can try to count all the square corners they can find in the room. (There are likely to be hundreds if they count each corner of every book!)

Group 3: These children should make more square corners with paper and see what happens when they put 4 square corners 'nose inwards' together. Can they put 5 together? (No.)

 Plenary session

✦ The focus group can demonstrate their moving arms of Meccano. Show how a 4-sided shape with sides all the same size will sometimes have square corners but can be squeezed up so that it becomes a diamond without square corners.

✦ Let children demonstrate where they found square corners. Group 3 might have found that if you fit 4 square corners together you fill up all the space.

✦ Link square corners to movement. The children stand up and move one quarter turn/one square corner and so on. Continue this in PE.

LESSON TWO
PIRATE MAPS

 Assessment focus

Can the children give instructions for someone else to follow their route?

 Resources

✦ items such as a skipping rope, cloth and boxes to make a 'map' of an island
✦ toy to hide, such as a play person

Oral work and mental calculation

Describing a route

✦ Lay out some features on the carpet to make an island, such as a blue cloth for a round lake, a skipping rope as a river, a brick bridge and a tower to be a mountain (able to have something put on top of it), a box to be a house and a box to be a cave. The children take it in turns to put something – a play person or a treasure box – somewhere on the island, for example in the cave or beside the river. Ask questions or give directions about position: *"Put the parrot higher than/to the left of the person."* and *"Put the treasure box on the edge of the river."* Then make routes across the island, the children taking it in turns to describe what they are doing, or giving instructions to another child: *"Go clockwise round the lake."* and *"Go to the right of Dragon Mountain."*

Position, direction & movement

◆ Starting point: whole class

✦ Draw a large treasure map on paper like the one on the sheets. To give an authentic pirate look, pour cold tea on the paper and burn the edges.

✦ Describe some routes across the map as in the oral maths session: *"Start at Parrot Cove and go to Horrid Hill."* and *"Which way round Muddy Marsh do you want to go, anti-clockwise or clockwise?'*

✦ Let one child choose a secret place on the map to bury treasure. Ask *"I'm going across this river. Am I getting nearer to your treasure?"* You can develop this idea of moving across the map if you do a grid of squares. *"I'm in this square by Dragon Mountain and I'm going to go into this square."*

✦ Explain how pirates must make maps and write down their route when they bury their treasure or they might forget where they put it. Tell the children they are going to choose a place on a map to land and then bury their treasure. They must write down a route so they will be able to find it again. Many children at this age will have no difficulty in using grid references for maps once you have explained it.

◆ Group activities

Focus group

Work with children who are finding it hard to use position words such as 'higher' or 'to the left of' and

do the starter again with them. It is helpful to identify children who have orientation problems, especially those who muddle left and right. Putting a red dot on their right wrist can help them.

 Teacher independent groups

Use the photocopiable activity sheets.

Activity sheet 1: This is a simplified map and the children can either write the route or, if that is too hard, draw the route and tell it to their partner and then to you.

Activity sheet 2: These children should write the route to their chosen treasure site.

Activity sheet 3: Explain to these children that they must give very clear details, saying whether they go clockwise or anti-clockwise around lakes and so on. Encourage them to use grid references for where they hid their treasure and their route.

◆ Plenary session

✦ Let the children explain their routes, following them on your big map.

✦ They can secretly choose places on the map to bury some treasure and challenge their friends to guess where it is.

◆ Further activities

✦ Make an 'angle muncher' by folding a circle into quarters and cutting out one quarter.

✦ The children use this to test right angles by fitting the angle into the mouth and the angle muncher eats it. Use it also to test angles that are smaller or larger than 90 degrees.

✦ Play games where a child secretly chooses a square on the grid and other children have to guess it, writing their name in a square if they choose that square.

◆ Extension

✦ Make further maps using the grid references, for example a simple map of the school or the route home.

◆ Support

✦ Let these children use a floor robot and Logo as much as possible to give intensive help with angles and routes.

✦ Treasure map ✦

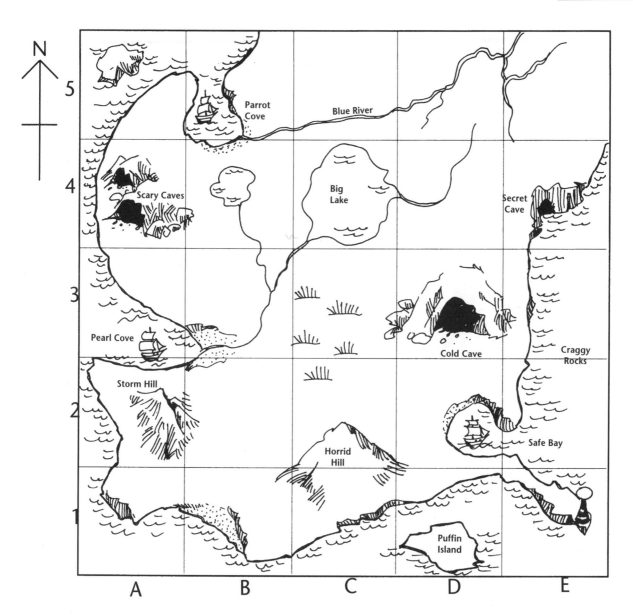

✦ Choose a place to bury your treasure.

Draw your ship where you landed.

Mark the route from your ship to the treasure.

 Draw your own treasure map.

Numeracy
Year 2/P3

developing
Numeracy
Skills

Photocopiable
©Hopscotch Educational Publishing
87

✦ Treasure map ✦

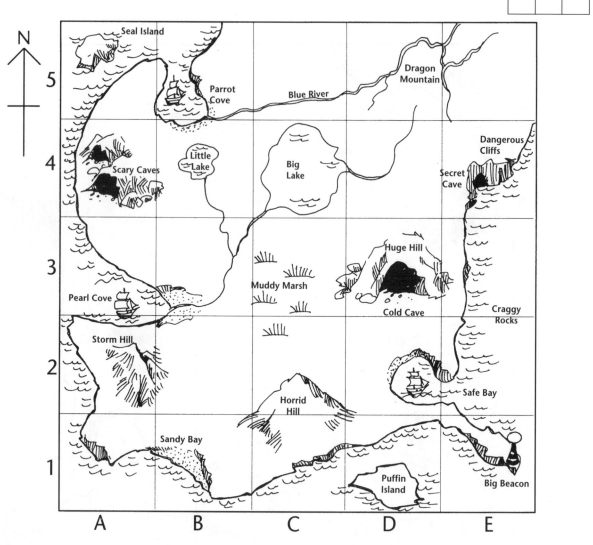

1. Choose a place to bury your treasure.

2. Write instructions for how to find your treasure.

Land at _____ Walk _____

 Draw your own treasure map.

◆ Treasure map ◆

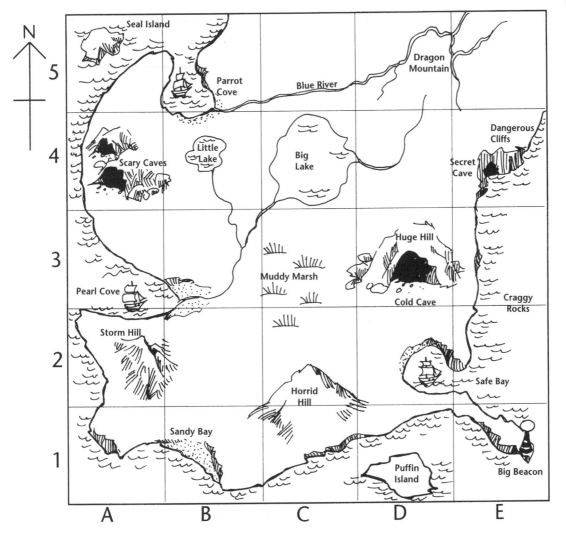

1. Choose a place to bury your treasure. Write the square it is in.

2. Write instructions for how to find your treasure.

Land at _____   Walk _____

 Draw your own treasure map.

Photocopiable
©Hopscotch Educational Publishing
89

◆ 100 square ◆

1	2	3	4	5	6	7	8	9	10
11	12	13	14	15	16	17	18	19	20
21	22	23	24	25	26	27	28	29	30
31	32	33	34	35	36	37	38	39	40
41	42	43	44	45	46	47	48	49	50
51	52	53	54	55	56	57	58	59	60
61	62	63	64	65	66	67	68	69	70
71	72	73	74	75	76	77	78	79	80
81	82	83	84	85	86	87	88	89	90
91	92	93	94	95	96	97	98	99	100

developing
Numeracy
Skills

Name _____

◆ Blank 100 square ◆

Name _____

◆ Number lines ◆

◆ Round and round ◆

+ 6

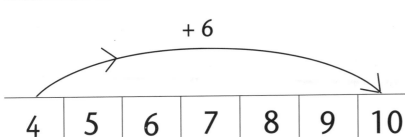

| 4 | 5 | 6 | 7 | 8 | 9 | 10 | 11 | 12 | | |

− 6

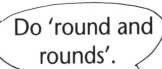

Do 'round and rounds'.

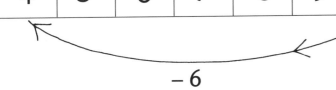

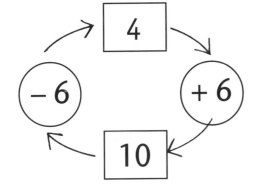

4

− 6   + 6

10

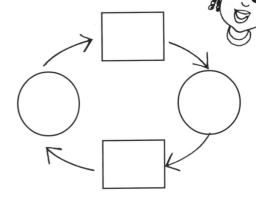

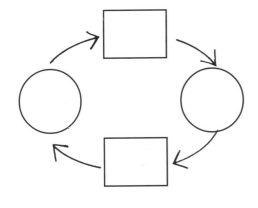

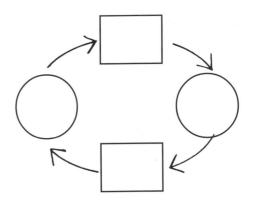

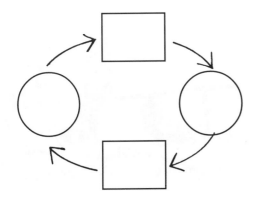

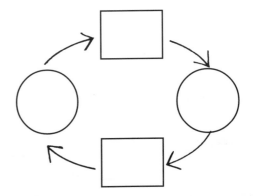

developing
Numeracy
Skills

◆ Treasure island – 1 ◆

developing
**Numeracy
Skills**

Name _____

◆ Treasure island – 2 ◆

START

developing
Numeracy Skills

Photocopiable
©Hopscotch Educational Publishing

✦ Self-assessment sheet ✦

	✔
I can order numbers to 100 and above to	
I know what each digit represents in numbers to 100 and above to	
I can describe and extend a pattern or number sequence.	
I can estimate positions on a number line.	
I know all the addition and subtraction facts to 10 /20 /	
I can show how addition 'undoes' subtraction on a number line.	
I can write subtractions and the related addition facts.	
I can split numbers to help me add and subtract.	
I can add/subtract 9 and 11 by adding/subtracting 10 then adjusting.	
I know numbers can be added in any order.	
I can choose from a range of ways of calculating and explain my methods.	
When I add 2-digit numbers I like to	
When I take away numbers I like to	
I know my 2 and 10 times tables.	
I know how to put out cubes in equal groups to do multiplication.	
I can tell number stories and write the calculation with the right operation.	
I can read a scale.	
I can measure carefully with a ruler.	
I can solve a problem by collecting data to help me answer the question.	
I can describe 2D and 3D shapes and I know some of the names.	
I know lots of words to describe positions, routes and movement.	
I can	
I can	
I can	
I can	
I want to get better at	
and	

©Hopscotch Educational Publishing